MAKING LOVE

First published in 1992 by Hamlyn,
an imprint of Reed Consumer Books Limited
Michelin House, 81 Fulham Road, London SW3 6RB
and Auckland, Melbourne, Singapore and Toronto

Reprinted 1992

A catalogue record for this book
is available from the British Library

ISBN 0 600 57443 1 (hardback)
0 600 57445 8 (paperback)

Printed in Portugal

MAKING LOVE

BECOME A MORE SENSUAL LOVER

LINDA SONNTAG

HAMLYN

CONTENTS

INTRODUCTION

Since the 1960s, when the advent of the Pill created a climate of greater sexual awareness, the laws governing divorce, abortion and homosexuality have been relaxed, and today there are more single parents and more children born outside marriage than ever before. Marriage itself is on the decline, and so is religion, and with it the concept of sin. We are witnessing the gradual breakdown of rigid attitudes towards human relationships, and the beginning of opportunity for greater freedom and self-expression in our personal lives. At the same time, we are faced with the threat of AIDS, which discourages sexual experimentation. Our sexual liberty has increased, but so have the dangers, both emotional and physical, attendant on sexual choice.

To help us find our way through the maze of modern relationships, sexologists such as Shere Hite, today's greatest gatherer of information on the subject, and behavioural scientists such as Desmond Morris, have compiled exhaustive data on human sexuality. Without their work it would be impossible to write about sexual experience in general terms. But the difference between absorbing this information and diving into the living reality of a sexual relationship is like knowing the sea from a navigation chart, then suddenly being plunged into it. There can be no adequate preparation.

Making love is the most personal of human activities and, unlike putting up shelves or building a patio, it cannot be learned from a book. No matter how much we absorb from reading and looking at pictures, and even from talking to other people, the ability to love and satisfy another person can only really be learned from inside. Yet in the last 30 years, the demand for books on the subject of sex has been growing. People are adventurous, and curious about the sex lives of others, so they look at sex books for ideas; they are anxious to discover whether their own sexual pleasures and problems are 'normal', so they look for comparisons and reassurance; and they are concerned about medical or emotional aspects of sex, so they look for advice. The three sections of this book aim to cater to these three different needs.

The Sexual Relationship

Our attitudes to sex and sexuality are shaped both by the society and the age in which we live, and by the influence of our immediate family. Understanding the roots of our feelings enables us to overcome inhibitions and form deeper and more satisfying sexual relationships.

ATTRACTION

What is it that suddenly makes two people light up the instant they set eyes on each other? Why does it often take only a few seconds of being in each other's company for a man and a woman to feel irresistibly drawn together? One moment you may be leading a normal, seemingly uneventful life, and the next, you may find yourself exchanging glances with someone who makes you feel bewildered, excited, elated, charged with nervous energy. Moments such as these never fail to catch us unawares, and their force and suddenness can change the whole course of our lives.

To an onlooker, the phenomenon of sexual attraction often resembles nothing so much as madness. Within a short time of meeting, two rational people are capable of promising to stay together for upwards of half a century. The lovers themselves may be too impatient to analyse how they can possibly be so sure of each other; it is enough for them to be in love, and they are content to attribute their new-found state of high excitement to immense good fortune.

Because sexual attraction is instant, it seems involuntary, and therefore is often put down to a superhuman agency such as 'luck' or 'destiny'. Mythology would have us believe that attraction is directed by the gods and that it strikes out of the blue in the form of Cupid's fatal dart. The magic potion on the tip of the dart suspends consciousness, will and judgement, and leaves its victims in a state of hopeless intoxication.

It is still commonly believed today that sexual attraction is something irrational and beyond our power to influence or control, yet studies made by psychiatrists and behavioural scientists have found that it is far from being the random and inexplicable phenomenon that it seems. Newly published evidence suggests that we are unconsciously, and at a glance, capable of making fairly accurate judgements about not only other people's social and economic standing, but also about their emotional background. The 'miracle' of love at first sight really does exist, but what is truly miraculous is our own unconscious process of selection.

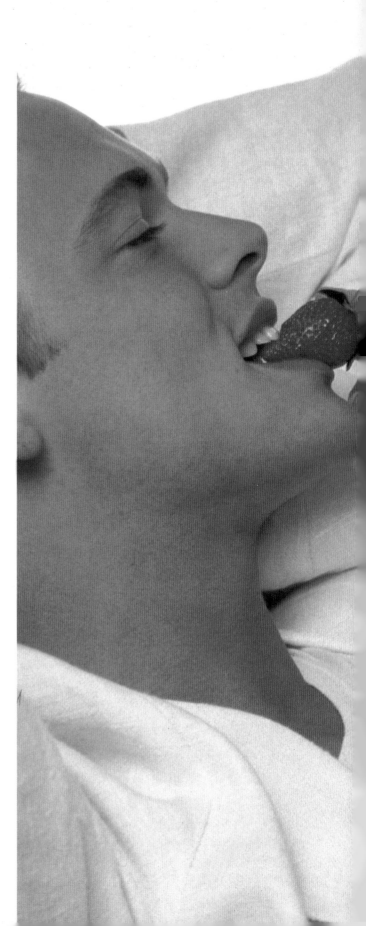

THE CHEMISTRY OF ATTRACTION

It is commonly believed, and has been borne out by many successful partnerships, that opposites attract. Introverts and extroverts are often drawn together because the quiet strength of the one complements the liveliness of the other. The extrovert sees the introvert as a rock, an anchor in a storm; and the introvert sees the extrovert as fire, warmth and light. Their lives would feel incomplete without each other; they act as a unique foil for each other's characters; and they do not compete, because the sum of all their attributes seems to form a perfect whole.

Other partnerships show that like also attracts like, in terms of character, appearance, or family background. In every relationship there will undoubtedly be some points of similarity, and others where the partners are poles apart. Whether the relationship succeeds depends not only on getting the perfect balance, but also on keeping the balance as each partner grows and develops, possibly at different speeds and in different directions.

The Institute of Family Therapy carries out a fascinating experiment with its new recruits. Before the individuals in the group have got to know anything about each other, psychiatrist Robin Skynner asks them to walk around the room and, without exchanging any words, pick a partner whom they feel could be a 'missing member' of their own family. Each couple then selects a further couple to form 'families' of four. This process complete, Robin Skynner asks them to talk together to find out why they have picked each other. He is always amazed by the unerring way in which individuals can single out others with very similar family backgrounds. A group of four might find, for instance, that all their fathers spent a significant period of their childhood away from home, whereas another group might discover that the individuals all came from families where there was a difficulty with expressing affection or anger, or where everyone was expected to 'keep a stiff upper lip' and to conceal their true emotions.

The exercise demonstrates that people are drawn together because of similarities in the way in which their families functioned, but the knack we have of recognizing these similarities, just by looking at another person, is uncanny. How do we do it? Robin Skynner explains the mysterious 'chemistry' of attraction by saying that our childhood experiences – the reactions we learned to give in various situations – have over the years 'hardened' into habitual expressions, gestures, postures and movements, and it is these signals to which we respond as adults. Thus someone who was punished habitually as a child might look wary, evasive, guilty, cringing or sullen, and another person with the same experience will be able to recognize the root of these expressions straight away. Likewise, someone who was denied parental affection might look worried, insecure, round-eyed and lost or clinging, and again these qualities will be immediately apparent to someone with shared experience.

In our quest for the familiar we also seek out the same faults or weaknesses in other people that played a formative role in our own childhood. The writer Edna O'Brien put it like this: 'I have a big flaw in that I am attracted to thin, tall, good-looking men who have one common denominator. They must be lurking bastards.' If a loved father harbours a lurking bastard, then love will always be associated in the mind of the child with a tendency towards cruelty. When the child grows up, the chances are that she will find herself attracted to men who display this irresistible characteristic.

When two pairs of eyes meet across a crowded room and an instant decoding of the signals leads to a leap of recognition, a conversation normally follows, and both parties are astounded to discover how much they have in common. The seeds of shared preferences – in politics, lifestyle, music and any other field – will have been sown in childhood and fertilized by parental approval, or even fuelled by parental disapproval. It is not uncommon for people who have only just met to say rapturously: 'I feel as though I've known you all my life!', and Robin Skynner's experiment shows that this is not just fanciful romanticizing.

APPEARANCE AND GOOD LOOKS

A more obvious factor in the complex signals of sexual attraction is a person's physical appearance. However, contrary to popular belief, people are not automatically attracted to the most beautiful member of the opposite sex, although there is broad agreement as to what constitutes physical beauty in men and women. Instead, they are drawn to people who are in the same league of attractiveness as themselves.

Two experiments illustrate this. In one, a group of people, some of whom were physically attractive and others less so, were shown a series of photographs and asked to select the person with whom they would most like to go out. Only the most attractive people picked beautiful partners. In the other experiment, people were given individual photographs of men and women who were married. They were asked to rate them on a scale of ten for good looks, and then to place them in pairs. Most agreed roughly on the degree of attractiveness of each individual, and most of the pairs shared the same rating; remarkably the group had put together several couples who really were married.

But although plain men and women were attracted to one another, the group was inclined to assume that better looking people had more socially desirable attributes. The experiment showed that we associate an attractive appearance with success, not just in love. This attitude gives attractive people an enormous boost in self-confidence, and confident people, however good looking, have more chance of experiencing instant sexual attraction.

THE BODY'S SECRET SIGNALS

A group of men were shown a poster featuring the face of an attractive girl. They were then shown a second poster, which was identical in all respects except for one hardly noticeable alteration. Asked to choose which of the posters appealed to them most, the majority chose the second, but they were at a loss to say why. On the second poster, the pupils of the girl's eyes had been retouched to look larger.

When we are aroused, our pupils dilate. It is a signal of sexual attraction that is impossible to fake at will, and if someone you find attractive gazes at you with dilated pupils, the odds are

that this will spark interest, even if you're only looking at a photograph. This phenomenon was known to eighteenth-century Italian courtesans, who dripped deadly nightshade into their eyes to make their pupils dilate; the Latin name for deadly nightshade is *belladonna*, which means 'beautiful woman'. Curiously enough, self-confessed Don Juans – men who get their sexual pleasure from brief encounters with a string of women – prefer to look at photographs of girls with small pupils, which seems to confirm the fact that they fight shy of emotional warmth.

Sexual scent is another of the body's secret signals. The delicate natural odours of a warm, clean body are highly attractive to the opposite sex, but all too often these are masked by perfume or aftershave, or the scents in make-up and deodorant. Another more subtle range of body 'odours', which are not recognized by the nose but nevertheless detected by the brain, are called pheromones. The male pheromone androstenone is found in both sweat and urine, and in women pheromones known as copulins

are present in vaginal secretions.

Women produce larger quantities of pheromones around the time of ovulation, and this stimulates increased arousal in their partners. Male pheromones are so potent that they are able to disrupt the menstrual cycle. In all-female institutions, such as convents, it has been found that the menstrual cycles of the inhabitants gradually adjust until they coincide. When the pillows of some of the nuns in one convent were impregnated with male pheromones, they began to menstruate at a different time from the rest. Another experiment showed that chairs and telephones sprayed with male pheromones were constantly preferred by women to untreated ones.

Sexual attraction boosts the body's production of hormones, pheromones and vaginal secretions, and this potent sexual 'aura' is what French women call their *cassolette*. Far headier than the most expensive perfume, *cassolette* is a potent weapon in the armoury of every woman's sexual attraction.

BODY LANGUAGE

No one can write about this subject without acknowledging that it was practically 'invented' by Desmond Morris. In his book 'Manwatching', he explains that the language of the body – expressions, gestures, the way we stand and the way we move – is for the most part unconscious, as is our understanding of the body language of others. We don't have to think about it to realize that a man who is pinning a woman against a wall at a party and leering down her cleavage is showing aggressive sexual interest. Nor do we need a degree in psychology to work out that the woman, if she has her arms crossed over her chest and is frowning at him, does not welcome his attention. These two people are giving off signals loud and clear that cannot be misread.

Sometimes, however, through nerves or lack of confidence, we give off the wrong signals. If you go alone to a party hoping to meet interesting people and then sit hunched in a corner with your legs tightly wrapped around each other, your arms folded and your head lowered, you should not be surprised if people can't detect the friendly and talkative person you really are under your hostile exterior. The people who invite approach are the ones who stand and sit in a relaxed and open way and appear alert to their surroundings and unafraid to engage in eye contact. If you have the confidence to look as friendly and interested as you feel, conversation will practically initiate itself.

THE LANGUAGE OF ATTRACTION
Once contact has been made between two people who are attracted to each other, the signs come thick and fast. The eyes show vulnerability – a conflict between fear and desire. They want to look and, at the same time, to look away. If both people are shy, they will exchange only the briefest of glances to begin with, looking in between times fixedly at the carpet, or at their hands. Shy, sidelong glances often called 'sheep's eyes' follow, until one person gains enough courage to look for longer. As confidence grows, eye contact becomes more prolonged: couples stare at each other, and 'devour' each other with their eyes. They also begin to look at other parts of each other's faces, particularly at the mouth, and then at other parts of the body, but all the while checking back to the eyes to assess their partner's reactions to such scrutiny.

People who are interested in each other sit or stand facing each other, not sideways on, which indicates some reserve. Their attitudes to each other are open, with no barriers, such as arms across the body. Their faces are tilted towards each other with wide eyes and eyebrows raised, and they smile a lot with their mouths open. There are generally more gestures. Hands, arms and shoulders are employed to express vitality, as are eyebrows and lips, and the tongue is more active than usual, becoming a particular focus of attention. The pair will stand closer together than is normal, and at the slightest excuse there will be physical contact, usually in the guise of a gesture of support, such as helping a woman into a coat or protecting her from someone passing in a hurry.

As the conversation progresses with the exchange of shared likes and dislikes, there may be a temptation to suppress true opinions in order to avoid the danger of a disagreement bringing the budding relationship to a premature end. People who have just met and who like each other tend to nod a lot in enthusiastic agreement, even if their views diverge. But if the disagreements are fundamental, eventually these will put a dampener on the initial attraction. Other people who are more confident make playful use of argument to pepper their conversation, and this is particularly attractive to those who like bold and daring characters, though it may frighten off more timid prospective partners.

SIGNS OF COUPLING
In the early stages of a relationship, couples display strong signals that tell the world they belong together. Physical closeness – standing, lying or sitting together with or without touching – is the most obvious. It proclaims that

the pair share a common space, which others are not welcome to invade. Young lovers can often be seen embracing and kissing in public, and new lovers of any age touch each other frequently and are solicitously attentive to one another. There is constant gazing and prolonged staring into each other's eyes.

In the first stages of a relationship, before the couple have taken the decisive step of making love, there will probably be continuous animated conversation. The act of making love bonds the couple more securely, and now they will feel relaxed enough to lapse into periods of silence, merely sitting together basking in each other's company.

Much of the conversation in the initial stages of a relationship will reveal the past, so that each partner feels that he or she has shared in the previous life of the other. At the same time, they learn each other's reactions to events of the present. There comes a stage when the learning process is complete. Couples who have been together for many years often know instinctively what their partners think and feel. They do not need to ask, and can communicate confirmation of mutual understanding with the minutest glance or gesture. But for these small signs that they are attuned to each other, a couple of long standing might appear to the outside world as remote from each other as strangers.

SEXUAL SIGNALS

When a baby is born, only its genitals distinguish male from female, but as the child grows into an adult, it develops distinctive sexual characteristics that signal its gender to prospective mates.

As Desmond Morris explains, many of the body's gender signals have evolved over more than a million years. When early man began to depend more on hunting for food and less on the gathering of roots

and berries, labour was divided between the sexes. The females, who were almost always either pregnant or nursing their offspring, could not accompany the males in pursuit of game, and so the nomadic way of life was replaced by a settled one. The females continued to forage near the settlement for food, while the males roamed further afield. As the males got more adept at hunting, their bodies developed to suit its requirements.

Although in most parts of the world men no longer live by hunting and women's lives are greatly

less restricted by breeding, the past lives on in the bodies of modern man and woman. Men are taller, more muscular and heavier. They are built for running faster and for carrying heavier loads. They are broad-shouldered, with stronger arms, which makes them better equipped for using weapons. They have broader chests and larger lungs making them capable of greater exertion, and they have stronger skulls and jaws to protect them more efficiently against attack.

The special features of the female physique are her wider pelvis, which is tilted slightly backwards to facilitate child-bearing, her longer belly and thicker thighs, geared towards carrying the foetus, and her swollen breasts, developed for suckling her young. The wide pelvis means that the thighs start from further apart, and the female's crotch gap contrasts with the male crotch bulge. The angle of the legs, which slope together towards the knees, and the fleshy protuberances of breasts and buttocks, make running less easy than for the male. The narrower shoulders mean that the arms hang at the sides, *whereas the more muscular male stands with his arms hanging away from his body. The female physique is thus less well developed for carrying, but the female forearm can swing out from her side to a much greater angle than can that of a man.*

The differences in the structure of male and female arms and legs mean that each sex moves in a quite distinct way. It is something that we take for granted until a male comedian draws attention to it by mimicking a woman or an effeminate man.

DISPLAY SIGNALS

There are other sexual signals that have nothing to do with our evolutionary past as hunters and breeders. They act purely to emphasize the bearer's sex. The male has a deeper voice and a prominent Adam's apple. His body is generally hairier, although the hair on the top of the head may thin and disappear in later life. The female is characterized by a fleshier body, with smooth spherical breasts and buttocks echoed by rounder knees, shoulders and cheeks; fuller lips, and a softer, almost hairless skin.

It has been said that whereas the male

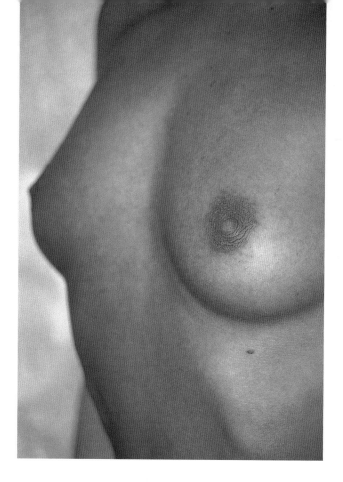

erogenous zones (parts of the body that respond to sexual stimulation) are primarily the genitals, mouth and hands, the entire female body is an erogenous zone, because the skin is so sensitive. In an effort to make their skin even more appealing to the opposite sex, many women shave their armpits and spend a great deal of money in beauty clinics having 'unsightly' body hair removed.

Display signals are used in the animal kingdom as a sexual invitation. The female monkey or ape signals her willingness to copulate by presenting to the male her rump and genitals, which are often highly coloured. Since adult humans normally encounter each other face to face, now that we no longer walk on all-fours, the female body has developed frontal display signs that are genital mimics. The rounded breasts are reminiscent of the buttocks, and the full lips represent the labia.

Women are well aware of the potent attraction of these genital mimics, as are commercial advertisers. To emphasize their sexuality, women are often photographed with reddened and moistened lips which are slightly parted. The message is made blatantly clear in

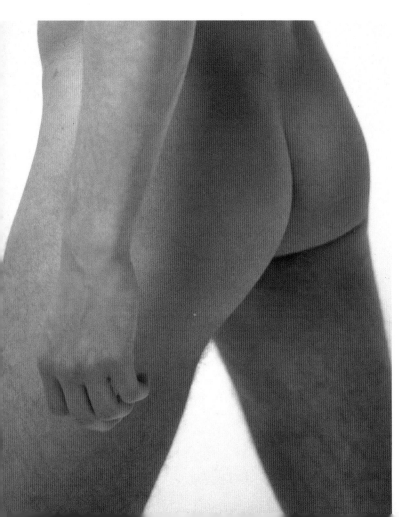

advertisements for lipstick or chocolate bars in which the phallic-shaped object is shown being held at the tantalizingly open mouth. In fact, women have been drawing attention to their lips by colouring them for over 4,000 years. Another trick that photographers use is to get their models to pose with a cheek pressed against a shoulder, or with knees, cheeks and shoulders all pressed against one another. The smooth spheres of flesh next to the glistening lips send out a powerful sexual message.

The male face can also be looked at in this way. Some artists have drawn attention to the resemblance between the male nose and the penis. The fleshy end of the nose could be said to bear a resemblance to the glans, and a cleft chin suggests the scrotum, while grizzled male facial hair is certainly more like pubic hair than head hair.

CLOTHING AND SEXUALITY

The first piece of clothing ever to be worn was the loincloth, and this was originally adopted when man began to walk upright. As soon as he got up from all-fours he exposed his genitals to everyone he met, and to eliminate the resulting inappropriate sexual signal, he concealed them behind a 'fig leaf '. The climate in which early man developed did not necessitate the wearing of clothes for protection against heat or cold, so the first garment was donned purely for reasons of modesty.

As man moved away from his early home into other climates, a wide range of protective clothing was adopted. Our clothing, today as always, reflects the attitude of the society in which we live towards sexuality. For example, in some Arab countries, women are swathed in voluminous robes from head to toe so that only their eyes are visible. It seems strange to note that only a century ago in Britain, a similarly repressive attitude was so all-pervasive that it even spread to items of furniture: the legs of pianos and tables were considered so shockingly suggestive that they were hidden in decent households under heavy cloths.

Clothing used to emphasize sexuality includes the brassiere, which pushes the breasts upwards and outwards and may offer padding as well as support, and the corset, another garment employed to alter the silhouette. The nineteenth-century practice of maids lacing their mistresses into excruciatingly tight bodices to accentuate their slender waists produced deformities of the ribcage and the internal organs, all in the cause of sexuality. Men have drawn attention to their brawny shoulders with shoulder pads and epaulettes, and to their genitals by the use of the codpiece, the sheathed gun or dagger at the hip, and even the sporran, with its mimic of pubic hair. Today, tight jeans over a bulging crotch give off the same message.

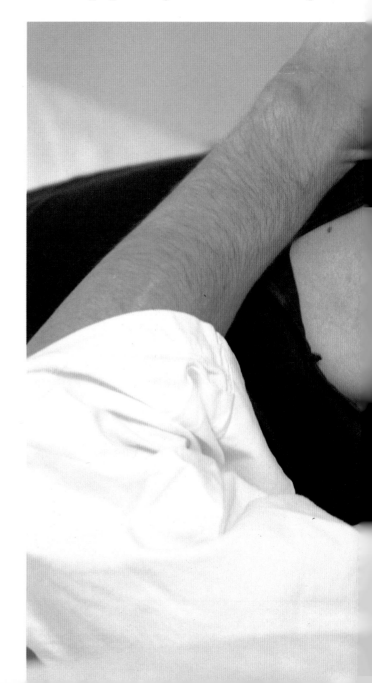

SHYNESS AND INHIBITIONS

Shyness of strangers has its roots in earliest childhood. Babies bury their heads against their mothers' shoulders when spoken to by unfamiliar people, young children hide in their mothers' skirts, while adolescent girls giggle and put their hands to their faces. Most adults still suffer some apprehension on moving into an unfamiliar social situation. To walk alone into a roomful of strangers engaged in animated conversation with each other and to integrate with them requires courage. The fear of being the outsider in a foreign territory is a strong one, and the newcomer usually expresses the need to protect himself against a strange environment by forming a barrier across his body.

Even the most confident person, on entering a restaurant or walking through a reception to greet his host, will fleetingly perform this action. It may take the form of fiddling with a cufflink or lapel, or of using the right hand to pull the left earlobe or scratch the left temple. Women frequently touch their hair, adjust their clothing, or check their bracelet, watch or bag. Men can often be seen entering a pub rubbing their hands together as they walk up to the bar. All these gestures, unconscious though they may be, form a temporary barrier across the body and betray the nervousness the newcomer feels.

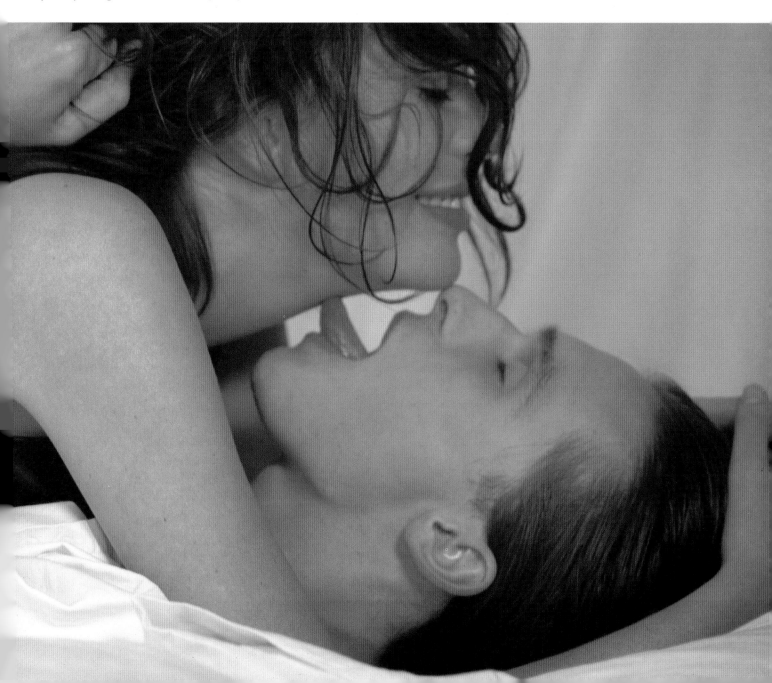

The shyness of the outsider needs to be conquered each time a new social situation is broached; the more practice you get, the better you will be able to disguise your nervousness.

THE TRUE MEANING OF 'INTERCOURSE'
Shyness resulting from a mixture of fear and desire characterizes the beginning of most sexual relationships, but after this has been overcome and the relationship is established, inhibition may still prevent true intimacy. A couple who are locked inside themselves, whether through fear or distaste of their own sexuality, or through lack of courage, imagination or knowledge, may copulate together throughout their married life without really communicating, and without ever properly getting to know the far reaches and deep subtleties of each other's personalities.

This situation suits some couples, but if one of the partners becomes more adventurous, he or she may seek the necessary stimulation elsewhere. True satisfaction comes not from travelling incognito on parallel rails, but from openness in all aspects of your life together. No one can expect to ignite the fire of passion without a spark, and you can't get sparks without friction, or friction without contact.

The word 'intercourse' means 'dealings in which there is an exchange of communication'. Sexual intercourse at its best is a communion in which feelings – physical and emotional – are freely given and received. A free exchange cannot take place if one or both partners are holding back.

SEX IS SIMPLY 'NOT NICE'
One of the reasons why some women never allow themselves to give free rein to their sexual feelings is because they have been brought up to believe that 'nice' women are basically sexless. One of the women who answered the questionnaires in *The Hite Report on Male Sexuality* had asked her father what a young man would think if she didn't give him a goodbye kiss on the doorstep. Would he think she didn't like him? No, said her father, he would think she was *a good girl*. 'I can't tell you the agony that

answer created in me,' wrote the woman, and there are many like her who feel that if they express their sexuality, 'nice' men will despise them and be disgusted by them.

Unfortunately, this attitude is self-perpetuating. Men who marry 'nice' women and put them on pedestals would not dream of behaving less than perfectly properly and respectfully to them in bed. Although consideration for one's partner is important in a good sexual relationship, politeness and formality are aspects of detachment and can have no part in intimacy. Reserve out of a misplaced 'respect' for one's partner leads to a suppression of fun, spontaneity and warmth. Sex for both partners becomes unimaginative and unsatisfying, though each may be craving to give and receive fuller satisfaction.

We are still living with the legacy of the Victorian era. Less than a century ago, decent married couples did not see each other naked; they undressed in darkness or in the privacy of separate dressing rooms, and nightgowns for both sexes were heavy and long. It was an English woman's marital duty to 'lie back and think of [increasing the population of] England', while her husband, as perfunctorily as possible, claimed his marital rights.

However, Victorian morality was two-faced, and because sexuality was banned from the marital bedroom (only procreation being allowed), it took place elsewhere, notably below stairs or in brothels. Married people today who suffer from socially imposed inhibitions that repress their sexuality may also look elsewhere to find more liberated and liberating partners.

'LETTING GO' IN BED
Fear of letting go is another major cause of sexual inhibition. To people who have been brought up with the idea that keeping control is the key to success in life, the very sound of the words 'letting go' represents chaos and disaster. This is as true of men as it is of women. Indeed, it is possible to go through the whole of the sex act, including orgasm, without ever giving oneself up to the other person. The result is,

'cold', mechanical sex.

Men who are sexually active but suffer from the fear of letting go rarely feel the need to feign passion, because erection and ejaculation are 'evidence' of their sexuality. However, for women, the situation is different. A woman may be desperate to show how attractive she finds her partner, and desperate to give herself, but prevented from doing so by her fear of letting go. In order to prove her sexuality, she may therefore act out what she thinks it means by thrashing about, moaning and groaning and even faking orgasms like the actresses in blue movies. (see p. 40).

Acting is exhausting, especially in bed, where you are very vulnerable and under close scrutiny. It is not satisfying because it erects a barrier between you and your partner, and if the problem is not tackled soon, it will simply drive you further apart.

BUT WHAT IS 'UNINHIBITED'?

Acting uninhibited is a far cry from being uninhibited. Being uninhibited is first and foremost being oneself. It is the very simplest thing, and yet, to the sexually inhibited, the most difficult.

The first step towards getting rid of your inhibitions is to relax. This is also often easier said than done. If told to relax, your partner

may well reply through gritted teeth that he or she *is* relaxed. The best way to relax is to try and stop thinking of sex as a performance. You are not on show. This is a private act, just between the two of you, and no one is sitting in judgement to give you marks out of ten. You are not out to achieve anything. Too many people are anxious about the climax before they begin. The man may be worried about losing his erection, the woman about not having an orgasm. Forget all that. Pleasure lies in the present, and you must live for the moment if you are to enjoy it.

Allow yourselves unlimited time and absolute privacy. Take things extremely slowly, savouring every touch and caress. Don't force anything, and if one of you feels that the other has made an artificial move – one that smacks of 'getting on with it' – gently stop him or her from continuing and re-establish your bearings. Being uninhibited is doing what you both like, and you are finding out exactly what that is, by moving very tentatively, as if you are exploring each other's bodies for the first time. Most of us like tenderness and gentleness; few like things they find unnatural or bizarre. Most people are touched by the admission of vulnerability, and touched by caring. So there is no need to be frightened. There is no possibility that you will suddenly lose control, because you are moving so very slowly, and paying so very much attention to each other.

Many people fear passion because, having experienced it only in their imagination, they think it will turn them into harlots or rapists. So they decide consciously to control it. By the time they meet somebody they really like, they may be accomplished in the mechanics of sex, but all feeling has gone out of the window. In order to get the full potential out of a good relationship, you must throw away your inhibitions. This involves not putting on an act, but stripping yourself bare of all pretence, and learning your own sexuality and that of your partner with all the curiosity and excitement and tenderness that you wish you had experienced when you lost your virginity.

TOUCHING AND CLOSENESS

Physical affection is an important form of emotional nourishment for the human baby. The drastic consequences of depriving babies of affection were shown in a study comparing the behaviour and development of babies in two orphanages. The parents of the babies in the first orphanage had been victims of an earthquake; the babies had been suddenly cut off from love and affection and there were not enough nurses to give them prolonged individual attention. These babies cried a lot and showed little interest in food. Their mental and physical development was slow. The babies in the second orphanage had been there since birth and were frequently picked up and cuddled by the staff. Their growth rate was normal, and they were alert and cheerful.

Babies and children thrive on being hugged and cuddled until they reach adolescence, when their developing bodies need privacy and separateness more than closeness. But once they emerge from puberty reorientated as young adults, they begin to seek contact with the opposite sex. Children who grow up in homes where physical affection is a natural part of everyday life usually have few inhibitions as adults about touching and closeness, and little trouble in recreating the warm, nest-like security of their early years in which to form an adult erotic relationship.

WHY PHYSICAL AFFECTION IS IMPORTANT FOR GOOD SEX

To completely envelop your partner in your arms and hold him or her tight in a generous hug is to affirm and accept the way that person is. Hugging and squeezing, holding hands, stroking faces and rubbing backs need not be sexual. In fact, these actions are more often loving, friendly, supportive, comforting, or just part of fooling around. If affectionate contact is part of the way you communicate with your partner, then expressing and receiving sexuality will be easy and natural. One man who answered questions in *The Hite Report on Male Sexuality*

wrote: '. . . the hug tells it all. I never could ask a woman to go to bed with me – I just "listen" to her body when I hug her, and I know.'

In the Bible, if two people have sex together, they are said to 'know' each other. This is no mere euphemism, but an accurate description of good sex. It is quite possible to copulate with someone for years without really 'knowing' who that person is, or feeling 'known' yourself. It is like striking the keys of a piano. Anyone can make sound come out, but if you want to make music, you need to learn each note that the individual instrument can produce, and to discover how to put them together. People who learn about each other's bodies by closeness and physical affection can tell the moment a loving hug melts into an erotic one. Lovemaking develops spontaneously and naturally as they discover each other's sexual potential.

WOMEN LOVE BEING CARESSED

The entire surface of a woman's skin, being smooth, delicate and hairless, is highly sensitive and responsive. Women enjoy wearing soft and silky fabrics next to the skin, and they love being stroked and caressed by a gentle partner. Most of the women who answered Shere Hite's questionnaires stressed the importance of touching and closeness in their relationships with men and to their sense of wellbeing in general. 'A good hug is worth the world. It is so much more than words.' 'Long, gentle passionate encounters, with much touching and enthusiasm, give me a feeling of being *loved all over*.' Many mentioned the value of sharing closeness and warmth, the intense pleasure of a fiercely tight embrace, the bliss of falling asleep with bodies entwined, of snuggling up and talking quietly, of lying still and listening to the other person breathe.

But according to some of the answers, the female skin is the world's most neglected erogenous zone. There was a frequent complaint that men were not naturally physically affectionate. Some men were reluctant to touch their partners unless sex was to follow. 'I only wish men could do this without it always and

only being a lead-in to sex. I don't think I would feel as used and frustrated all the time if there were any playing around, or signs of affection without it being in bed.' 'Men never want to touch and kiss without fucking.' Some women who craved affection had come to the conclusion that in order to get it, they would have to 'pay' for it with sex. And afterwards? 'After sex it is very depressing for me if there is no hugging and kissing. I feel like a discarded shoe. But most men don't like to do this.'

DON'T MEN LIKE IT TOO?

When children are little, boys and girls receive equal amounts of hugging and cuddling from their parents. But as they get older, boys in our society are taught that it is weak to show emotion. In order to grow into big strong men, they must choke back their tears and keep a stiff upper lip. It is fine for girls to weep for sadness or joy, to kiss and embrace, to be effusive and demonstrative, but boys must restrict themselves to handshakes, and, at the most, a pat or a slap on the back.

This means that while women often kiss and hug their friends, the only place where it is acceptable for men to show affection for each other is on the football pitch; and while most women long for close loving contact with their partners, fewer men can break out of the tactile isolation in which society has imprisoned them in order to give or receive it.

Almost all the men who answered Shere Hite's questions had reservations about touching and closeness, even though many recognized the importance of physical contact for women. Some men disliked women 'hanging round' them, which they saw as a sign of insecurity. Some were embarrassed to show affection out of a fear of 'not appearing masculine enough' or being 'childish'. But most said that affectionate behaviour was important only as a prelude to sex. 'Affection, touching, hugging, talking, kissing, are all meaningless and uninteresting unless there is some hope that they will eventually lead to sex.' One man said 'I don't like playing around for nothing.'

A common complaint among the men interviewed was that women who want affection for its own sake fail to take into account the ease with which men get sexually aroused. 'I wish sometimes I could experience pure affection. But I get turned on unbelievably quickly when I just intend to neck and do nothing else. I can't help it.' And another man said: 'What drives me up the wall is a woman who wants to climb all over you, give you a hard-on, and repeatedly do nothing about it. This turns affection sour. This is one of the areas, I think, where men and women have to do the most work understanding each other.'

RECONCILING TWO POINTS OF VIEW

The dissatisfied men and women quoted above have one problem in common: they categorize

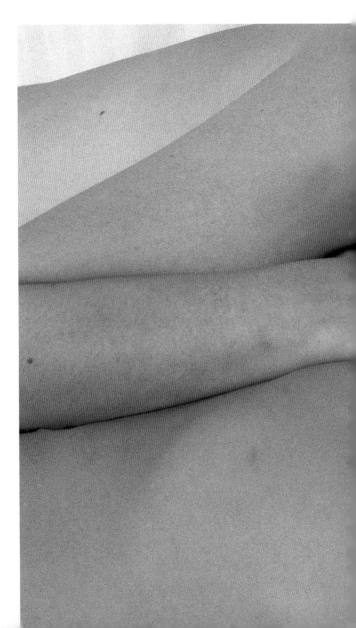

their feelings. The frustrated women draw a firm line between affection and sex. They feel cheated if they can't have the first without the second. The frustrated men also put their feelings in boxes, but they lump sex and affection together. For them however, it's either hands off, or all the way, no compromise. These rigid views are poles apart, and can cause a great deal of unhappiness.

Our feelings don't belong in boxes. They can't be turned on and off at will, as if by flicking a switch. It is ignorant and hurtful for a man who behaves coldly to a woman all day to expect her to be hot the minute they get into bed, and it is equally ignorant and hurtful for a woman to inflame a man and then, when he wants sex, leap away as though she'd been burned. There are many degrees of affection and

sexuality, and each stage grows out of the one before. For a couple who are physically and mentally in touch, it is possible to sense these moods as they develop, and to go with them, if the time is right, or to check them without rejection, but with the promise of later fulfilment, if the time is wrong.

One man described how he and his partner had found the ideal of closeness in their relationship. 'We are often affectionate, even in the presence of our children . . . we sleep together nude, we cuddle at night, and in the morning. When either of us feels the need, urge or desire for more intimacy . . . we read each other's body signals and just "drift into" (spontaneously) more pleasure tension – right on through to orgasm. For the majority of times, physical affection and touching are sufficient.'

FIRST-TIME SEX

Losing one's virginity is rarely a sensual experience. The novice is bound to feel nervous and afraid of the unknown as well as excited, but the dominant emotion is likely to be intense curiosity. It can be such a momentous event that often the identity of the first-time partner is not as important as the loss of virginity. Even though the sex may be bungled – over very quickly if the man is a virgin; slightly uncomfortable if it is the woman's first time – there will probably be a sense of relief afterwards, and even elation, that this important step towards sexual maturity has been successfully negotiated.

There are different things at stake on subsequent first times with other lovers. Unless it is a casual encounter, the focus will not be on oneself, but on the potential for togetherness. Curiosity about one's own body is replaced by desire for the other person's. The more intense the desire, the more nervous the lovers are likely to be. Although there are exceptions, first times rarely give more than an inkling of the sensuality the relationship may have to offer. It is difficult to guard against disappointment when highly aroused, but if the occasion does turn out to be a flop, you should at least be ready to console each other and try again.

WHAT IS THERE TO BE NERVOUS ABOUT?

Most people are apprehensive about appearing naked in front of each other for the first time. They fear that their imperfect bodies will be subjected to critical scrutiny and found wanting. Women imagine their breasts are too small or their thighs or abdomens too fat to be desirable, while men worry about puny chests and flabby bellies. The biggest male worry is the size of the penis (see p. 35), and though most feel that their one is too small, men who are very well endowed can also be embarrassed by the revelation of an extra-large organ. However, the better the couple know and like each other and the more tentative explorations they have made of each other's bodies before the first full encounter, the less afraid they will be.

The main problem that first-time couples are likely to have to face is that the man may be so nervous that he cannot get or maintain an erection. In which case, his natural frustration, distress and humiliation are made much worse by the importance of the occasion. Faced with the consummation of his desire, he has proved himself impotent, which is all the more galling if it has rarely or never happened before. The woman suffers too. She may feel frustrated, she may doubt that he really wants her after all, but if she really cares for him, her greatest difficulty will be in deciding how to cope with his distress. She can hardly ignore the situation and pretend that nothing is wrong, and trying without success to stimulate an unresponsive penis is likely to increase feelings of alienation and failure and may even cause resentment.

The best course of action is to stop 'trying', and to just hold each other and lie close. Too much overt sympathy on the part of the woman could be interpreted as condescending. After a while, one or the other of you will start talking. As the flaccid penis is most likely to be a temporary problem, the important thing is not to analyse it or worry about it, but to give basic reassurance that you still both like each other. Get up and fetch a drink. Enjoy your new-found intimacy in the way you talk to, look at and touch your partner. Once you are both so relaxed as to have forgotten the problem, desire will probably take you unawares, and this time nerves will be less likely to intervene.

Another male problem that commonly occurs on a first time is that over-excitement triggers premature ejaculation. This is not quite such a blow for the man's self-esteem, especially if penetration has been achieved, but it will leave the woman feeling hurt and unsatisfied if his embarrassment brings the lovemaking to an abrupt end. After a short rest, the man should be ready to continue, and this time he can concentrate on fully arousing and satisfying his partner before he allows himself to come for a second time. (If premature ejaculation is a recurring problem, and not just due to nervous tension, see p. 152.)

BRIEF ENCOUNTERS

Not all first times lead to second times, and sometimes a casual encounter is all that is intended. Whereas a lighthearted fling on holiday or while travelling may be harmless enough, casual sex stands little chance of being good sex because it usually takes place between strangers who have little knowledge of or interest in each other. There is an increased danger of disease, and a condom should always be worn to protect against VD and AIDS (see p. 136), as well as pregnancy. For women, there may be a risk of violence, or other unwanted behaviour. Emotionally, casual sex can leave feelings of worthlessness and emptiness. If you have a regular partner, a casual infidelity is likely to be followed by guilt.

People who feel driven from one brief encounter to the next are often very insecure, though they may seem confident when they boast about their conquests. They may have been unloved in childhood; still desperate for affection and approbation, they have sex in order to prove themselves wanted, but move on quickly for fear of rejection. The solution for someone who suffers from this problem is often to be found through counselling, which can restore a sense of self-worth and make it possible to form lasting attachments that bring both love and sexual fulfilment.

THE PHALLUS

At Khujarao in India around the year 1000, eighty three temples were built to glorify the gods. They were adorned with frieze upon frieze of figures depicting princes and concubines, courtiers and dancing girls, engaging in tender acts of love or experimenting with some of the more curious positions recommended by the 'Kama Sutra'. In contrast to the gaiety of the friezes, deep inside the temple, in the inner sanctum or 'womb house', the great god Shiva, lord of fertility and reproduction, appeared in symbolic form as a lingam or phallus, sometimes alone, and sometimes in conjunction with his consort Parvati, the vulva. When the British ruled India, they viewed these sculptures and the legends that surrounded them with the utmost horror and distaste.

The phallus has always been, and will continue to be, a symbol of potent fascination. All over the world and throughout history, it has been portrayed as the tree of life, the fount of creativity and the root of fertility. It stands not only for sex, but also for conquest, defiance, and protection against the evil eye – a phallic symbol is a magical, multi-purpose obscene gesture in both Eastern and Western cultures. The word 'phallus', signifying an erect penis, comes from the Greek; the Latin word for it was 'fascinum', which had the additional meaning of 'magical spirit'. However, most dictionaries nowadays prefer to dwell on the magical rather than the phallic when giving a definition of our modern word 'fascinate'!

THE QUESTION OF SIZE

In *The Hite Report on Male Sexuality*, Shere Hite reports that of the 7,239 men who answered her questionnaire, most men 'wished over and over again that their penis could be just a little larger'. One man wrote: 'Men with large penises make me feel threatened and inferior. It makes me think that a big cock must work better, and that's what women *really* want, because even if they don't say it or admit it, I imagine that a woman [is with] a man because he has a big cock and can protect her.'

The sexologists Masters and Johnson measured the flaccid penises of 300 men. The largest in their survey was found to be 13·75cm/5½in from the root, measured along the stomach side, and the smallest 5·5cm/2¼in. But while the average flaccid penis measures just under 10cm/4in, the average erect phallus is around 15cm/6in: in other words, smaller penises are capable of greater expansion. Contrary to popular belief, it is not true to say that you can tell the size of a man's penis by his height, the length of his nose or any other physical characteristic, including the colour of his skin.

Penis size can be something of an obsession. Men with smaller than average penises may feel anxious about their sexual prowess, and insecure in other aspects of their life, whereas men with 25cm/10in 'whoppers' may be over-confident. It was probably Mae West who said in appreciation of men who are less well endowed that it makes them try harder in bed, but is there anything in the old myth that a man with a bigger penis makes a better lover?

To men, bigger penises represent increased virility and powers of protection. However, according to surveys of women who have had several sexual partners and compared large and small penises in action, there are factors other than penis size which make the difference between good and bad sex. The truth is that the vaginal passage can stretch to allow a baby to pass through it, but it can also contract to hold a sanitary tampon in place. Similarly, it can expand to accommodate a large penis, and adjust to fit a small one.

This is not to say that some women may not have a preference for both the look and the feel of a large penis. Experiments have been carried out to measure the dilation of women's pupils when shown photographs of naked men and have proved that although society does not find it acceptable, women are just as aroused as men by the sight of a well endowed nude of the opposite sex. And it would be strange indeed if women were left unmoved by the fascination of the phallus.

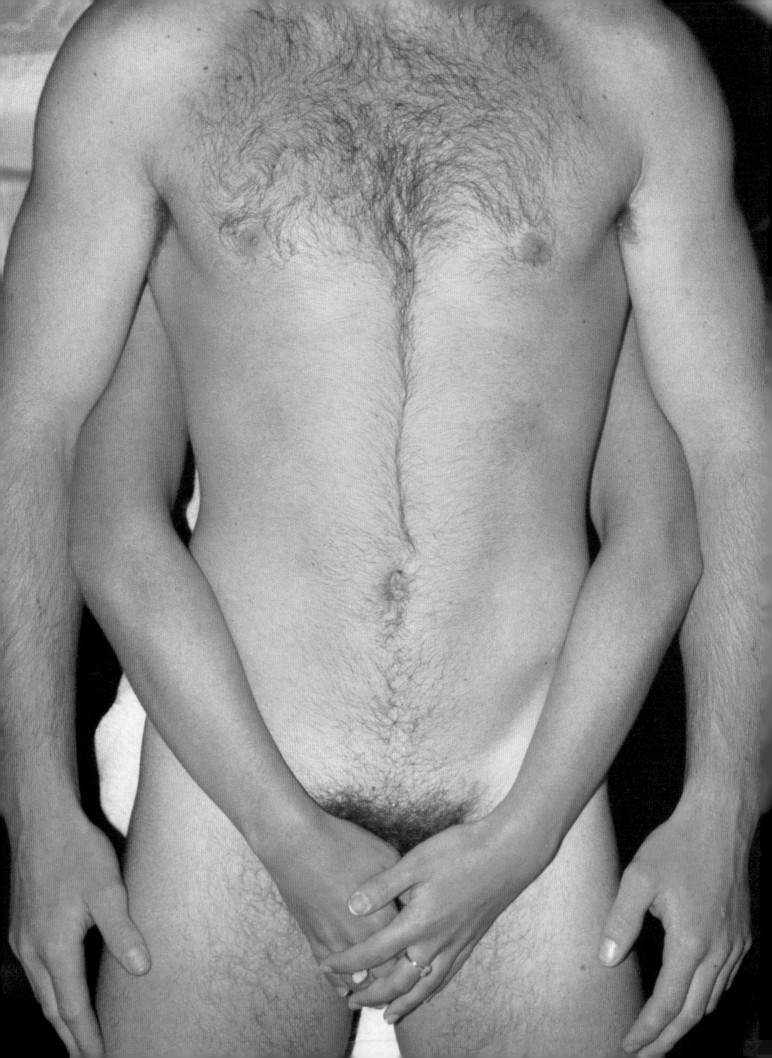

THE MIRACULOUS EXPANDING PENIS

Man has the largest penis of any living primate. Unlike the penises of most other mammals, it contains no bone, and relies for the stiffness needed for penetration on three rods of spongy erectile tissue, which respond to stimulation. The equivalent organ in the woman is the clitoris, which is also made of erectile tissue. During arousal, the tissue is engorged with blood, and muscles around the veins contract, producing an erection. A man cannot urinate with an erection because these muscles also close the urethra, the outlet from the bladder.

Erections are largely uncontrollable and can sometimes get their owners into embarrassing situations. Erections can be triggered not only by physical and visual stimulation, but also by the chafing of tight clothes or the vibration of public transport; they are often induced by fantasizing and may occur during sleep up to five times a night, each lasting for around 30 minutes.

During arousal a thick slippery lubricant is secreted by Cowper's glands, which are situated in the forward part of the urethra, and a droplet of this substance, appearing at the slit-like opening on the tip, or glans, of the penis may be mistaken for an early seepage of seminal fluid. In fact, it is there purely to facilitate penetration.

In uncircumcized men the glans is partly covered by the loose, thin, smooth and highly sensitive skin of the penis, which is moved back and forth over the shaft during sexual activity. In circumcized men the foreskin has been removed by a surgical operation, usually at birth. Circumcision or the lack of it makes no difference to sexual pleasure; uncircumcized men should pay particular attention to genital hygiene by regular washing under the foreskin, which may trap dirt and harbour infection.

THE MECHANICS OF EJACULATION

At the point of ejaculation a series of powerful muscular contractions causes semen to spurt from the tip of the penis. There is usually 2-5ml (up to a teaspoonful) of this sticky milky white fluid, of which the sperm content is only two to five per cent. Quantity of semen is no indication of fertility, but if there is less than 1ml, there is a possibility that the sperm will not reach the cervix through lack of liquid.

The sperm resemble microscopic tadpoles, although eighteenth-century biologists imagined that they could see minute versions of grown men and women swimming about in the seminal fluid. Semen also contains 32 different chemicals, including vitamin C, vitamin B12, sulphur, zinc and potassium; the Russian Empress Catherine the Great used to swear by it as a morning tonic. The purpose of all this goodness is to nourish the sperm as they make their perilous journey towards fertilization. The seminal fluid acts as a lubricant. The male orgasm lasts about 10 seconds, and it is possible, albeit unusual, to have an orgasm without ejaculation and, conversely, to ejaculate without having an orgasm.

As arousal intensifies, pulse and breathing speed up, and with ejaculation the body may be suddenly bathed in sweat, if it was not beforehand. Afterwards, the body returns to its natural state, the muscles at the base of the penis relax and the blood drains away, leaving the erectile tissue flaccid once more.

At around the age of 20, a man may not have to wait longer than a few minutes before getting another erection, and occasionally the penis does not wilt at all, but remains hard ready for a second session. Older men, on the other hand, usually take at least 20 minutes before they can become aroused again.

THE TESTICLES

The testicles are egg-shaped glands which hang in the scrotal sac beneath the penis. They are located outside the body because they need a temperature lower than that of the body for the successful production of sperm. In the cold, the muscles of the scrotum contract, so that the testicles appear to shrivel as they are drawn closer to the body for warmth. The testicles are acutely sensitive and very vulnerable: not all men like their testicles to be touched during lovemaking, and being hit in the balls produces an excruciating pain.

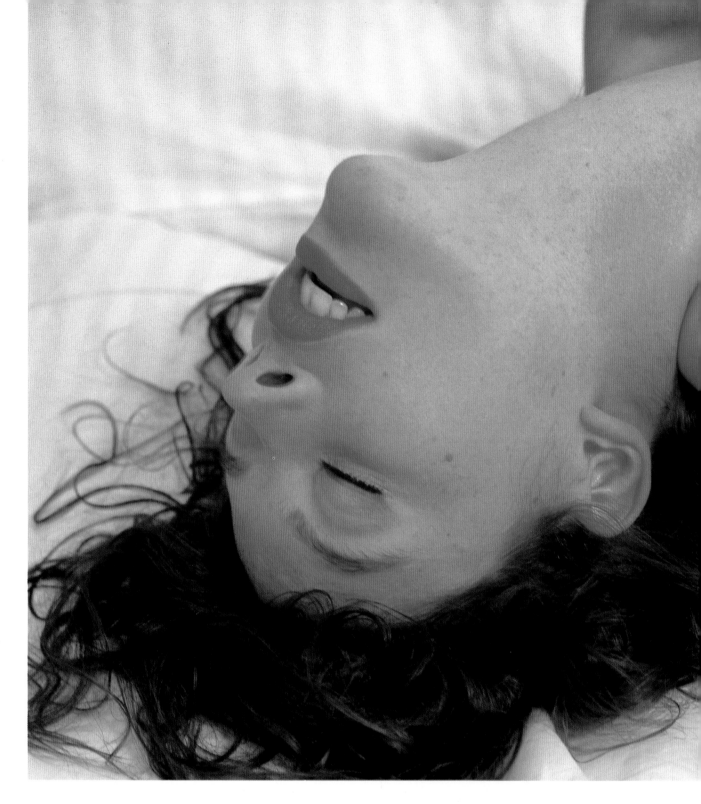

THE FEMALE ORGASM

Puritanically minded people have long argued that sex for pleasure is 'against nature'; they say that sex is 'meant' for the sole purpose of procreating the human race. If this is true, it follows that artificial methods of contraception are also wrong, because they allow sex for its own sake. Repressive views like these have been responsible for the fact that until quite recently in the West, the female orgasm was largely unacknowledged. The sexuality of women in other parts of the world is not merely unacknowledged – it is brutally denied. In a recent survey in Egypt conducted by the Cairo Family Planning Association, 90 per cent of the young women interviewed had had some part of the clitoris

and labia surgically removed. Female 'circumcision' had been carried out in an attempt to stop women enjoying sex and put an end to promiscuity.

Unlike the male orgasm the female orgasm is not necessary for procreation and exists purely to give pleasure, but this does not mean it is biologically useless. The sexual pleasure that two people find in each other produces an extremely powerful bond. Human beings have the strongest bonding potential of all animals, and it is no coincidence that they also produce the most demanding offspring. Sexuality provides the incentive that offsets the enormous responsibility of bringing up young.

In other species of primates, where the young quickly become capable of looking after themselves, mating occurs only at ovulation. In humans the female is always potentially sexually responsive, except for a brief period around giving birth. Unlike *apes and monkeys, humans are capable of prolonged sex play in which they can maintain high levels of arousal, and as far as researchers can tell, woman is the only female animal capable of orgasm. This peak of sexual enjoyment is a unique evolutionary development, which, when shared, can form the core of an intense and uninhibited relationship.*

AROUSAL

Sexual arousal is the highly sensitive state in which orgasm is possible. The women who answered Shere Hite's questionnaires were rapturous about arousal. They described it as a state of heightened awareness, mentally, physically and emotionally. They wrote of exhilaration, alertness, a fainting feeling, rushing urgency, supreme sensitivity, emotion, well-being, power, strength, freedom, gorgeous pleasure and ecstasy.

The first physical sign of sexual arousal is that the vagina secretes a lubricating fluid. Then the clitoris, the primary organ of female sexuality, a tiny hypersensitive nodule under the labia and above the vaginal opening, becomes hot, erect and swollen. With increasing arousal the labia or vaginal lips become engorged with blood – they look red and swollen and feel hot and slippery, tender and sensitive. In fact, the female sex organs expand during arousal to match the size of an average-to-large erect penis. The difference is that the responsive tissue in a woman is not as obvious as a man's erection, because it is hidden from sight.

All this can happen without genital contact, in the same way that a man's penis can become erect without being touched. Women can become aroused by psychological stimuli and by being kissed and caressed on any part of their bodies, although the mouth and breasts are particularly sensitive. The exquisite pleasure of arousal lies in its gradual intensification, and a skilful lover will excite his partner to a pitch where her genitals are engorged and lubricated before stimulating them directly with fingers, tongue or penis.

As arousal heightens, the woman's pulse rate speeds up, her body may arch, her muscles tense

and her blood pressure rises. Her face and chest may be flushed and pink, her nipples become erect and her breasts swell. Towards orgasm, the clitoris may become so sensitive that she can no longer bear for it to be touched. In the few seconds before she comes, the woman almost loses consciousness. She is concentrated inwards on herself, her muscles clench, and she may cry out as she loses herself in orgasm.

ORGASM

Women describing orgasm to Shere Hite wrote: 'Orgasm is the ultimate pleasure. . . .' 'They make me incredibly happy, everything on the way to orgasm is heavenly. . . .' 'A marvellous happiness, comparable to no other. . . .' 'The most fantastic sensation I've ever experienced.'

Orgasm, also called climax or 'coming', is a series of intensely pleasurable muscular contractions which, at the peak of stimulation, grip the engorged tissues surrounding the outer part of the vagina. The sexologists Masters and Johnson measured these contractions and discovered that they occur at intervals of four-fifths of a second – exactly the same rhythm as found in the contractions of the male orgasm. The number of contractions may vary from three to 12; in one particularly intense orgasm, 25 contractions were recorded over 43 seconds. The womb also contracts rhythmically, with spasms moving down in waves towards the cervix. Orgasmic contractions are similar to those experienced during childbirth, although, of course, they are far less severe.

Depending on his position, the woman's partner should be able to feel or see her vaginal contractions. External signs of orgasm in a woman are somewhat akin to rigor mortis, and may even be interpreted by an inexperienced lover as lack of interest. The woman's whole body becomes rigid and her hands and feet may clench. The blue-movie interpretation of female orgasm, in which women writhe, thrash, arch their backs and grind their pelvises against their partners is inaccurate: both women and men tense into stillness as they come. It is a moment of oblivion, a 'little death', as the French call it.

RESOLUTION

After orgasm, the woman's chest may be suffused with a red flush or rash. Unless further stimulation and more orgasms are to follow (see below), her body will now very gradually come down from its high to its normal state. Muscle tension relaxes; blood is released from the engorged tissues of the vagina; the clitoris subsides and withdraws under its hood; the uterus returns to its normal size; pulse, breathing and blood pressure all slow down.

This final phase in sexual response, which Masters and Johnson called 'resolution', may last for around half an hour and can hold feelings very precious for a woman. She may be overwhelmed by love and emotion for her partner to the point of shedding tears, or bathed in tenderness and wellbeing, or there may be a feeling of tremendous light-headedness, fun and vitality. Orgasm leaves women with shining eyes and full of happiness, and it is just as important for their partners to be able to share in this stage of their lovemaking as in any other. A woman feels let down and cheated by a lover who switches off after orgasm and leaves her to come down from her high alone.

Men are often criticized for the way they 'snap out of it' after sex, but there is a physiological reason for this. Men's bodies return within a matter of a few minutes to their unaroused state: breathing and heart rate normalize and the penis rapidly detumesces. Women do not return directly to their unaroused state, but to their pre-orgasmic state: they remain highly sensitive, and capable of further arousal.

Masters and Johnson discovered that women are capable of enjoying up to six successive orgasms, if they so wish. Some women feel fully satisfied after one orgasm, and the clitoris may be so sensitive that further stimulation is unpleasant or even painful, while others, and especially those who are used to giving themselves several orgasms in a row during masturbation, may crave more. Those who have multiple orgasms are not necessarily getting more enjoyment or satisfaction out of sex, and those who have single orgasms should not feel in any way inadequate. The important thing for both partners is to be aware that there is a choice (see Multiple and sequential orgasms, on p. 46). Shere Hite came to the conclusion that most women were unaware of their orgasmic potential which, she felt, explained why the overwhelming majority declared themselves fully satisfied with one orgasm.

WHAT IS 'NORMAL'?

A woman's sexual response is far more complex than a man's, and it varies considerably from one individual to the next. Some women are able to orgasm through passionate mouth-to-mouth kissing, or by having their breasts stimulated. The sexologist Kinsey reported that two per cent of his subjects could bring themselves to orgasm by fantasizing alone, although Masters and Johnson found none of theirs was able to do this. Kinsey discovered that eight per cent of his subjects orgasmed in their dreams. Masters and Johnson discovered that whereas less than 14 per cent of the women in their study had orgasms with a penis in the vagina, all the orgasmic women they investigated said they were able to climax with clitoral stimulation.

Both Shere Hite and Masters and Johnson found that a small proportion of women – about 10 per cent – never experienced orgasm. Their studies agreed, however, that in most cases the ability to orgasm could be acquired by learning to masturbate successfully, and by learning to relax in trust with a loving partner over a number of years. Kinsey noted that 63 per cent of women had orgasms with their partners in the first year of marriage, but that after 20 years together 85 per cent of women were orgasmic.

All the studies agreed that women experienced the most intense orgasms through clitoral stimulation – whether by masturbation or with a partner – and not through penile penetration. Kinsey found that only 37 per cent of women, as compared with 68 per cent of men, had experienced their first orgasm through masturbation. Nocturnal dreams were responsible for first orgasms in five per cent of

41

women and 13 per cent of men; petting in 18 per cent of women and five per cent of men; and intercourse in 30 per cent of women and 11 per cent of men.

Women were generally older than men and less experienced at masturbation when they had their first orgasm. In early adolescence, 95 per cent of boys were experiencing two or three orgasms a week, but only 22 per cent of girls had experienced orgasm at all. By their late teens, 99 per cent of boys and only 53 per cent of girls were having orgasms. By the time they were married, all Kinsey's male subjects had experienced orgasm, although 36 per cent of his female subjects had not.

VAGINAL AND CLITORAL ORGASMS

Are there two types of orgasm? It was Freud who first suggested that there were. He said that the orgasm experienced through clitoral stimulation was the precursor of a deeper, more satisfying orgasm experienced in the vagina during penetration by the penis. According to him, the vaginal orgasm was a 'true', 'mature' sexual response, while the clitoral orgasm was its immature inferior. The value judgements Freud and his followers placed on the two types of orgasm have caused a lot of unhappiness among some women who experience only clitoral orgasm, because they feel that they are missing out on 'the real thing', and are therefore inadequate: less than 'real women'.

Since Freud's time, researchers into sexual response have been much concerned with his categorization of female orgasm. Kinsey's view was that there was only one type of orgasm, that it was triggered by clitoral stimulation and involved contractions of all parts of the female body, including the vagina. He could not distinguish a second type of orgasm that centred solely on the vagina, and he utterly refuted Freud's distinction between 'mature' and 'immature' orgasms.

Subsequent clinical evidence has proved conclusively that Kinsey was right, and now sexologists are generally agreed that vaginal orgasm does not exist. Researcher Helen Kaplan

has come to this conclusion: 'Regardless of how friction is applied to the clitoris, i.e. by the tongue, by the woman's finger or her partner's, by a vibrator, or by coitus, female orgasm is probably always evoked by *clitoral* stimulation. However, it is always expressed by *circumvaginal* muscle discharge.'

All women who orgasm without penetration know the acute tension of the clitoris, the voluptuous rushing sensation that breaks into multiple contractions of the surrounding tissue. A small minority of these (around 20 per cent), who also orgasm with a penis inside the vagina, describe that as a quite different experience. Although Freud claimed that orgasms during intercourse were superior, the majority of women in Shere Hite's survey said they were less intense. 'Penetration orgasm is softer, more diffuse.' 'Intercourse orgasm involves the musculature of the abdomen more, gives more of a feeling of being shaken (like an earthquake) than being electrified, as clitoral does.' Whereas clitoral orgasm is experienced as a high, sweet, rippling sensation, the peak of sensitivity, orgasm with penetration is like the boom of a distant explosion, powerful, but somewhat muffled.

Orgasms triggered by the partner's fingers or tongue, and by masturbation, are probably more intense because stimulation is more localized and more sensitively guided. Masters and Johnson reported stronger contraction spasms and higher rates of heartbeat during orgasm without intercourse, and especially during masturbation, and many women confirmed that they had their best orgasms when alone. Orgasm during penetration is undoubtedly quite rare for many women because a thrusting penis can stimulate the clitoris only 'in passing', if at all, depending on the position of the couple. The orgasm experienced may be more diffuse because the penis alters the focus of attention from the clitoris to the whole of the lower part of the woman's body, and because the vagina is full, 'muffling' the sensation.

A simultaneous orgasm, when both partners come together during penetration, may feel like a surprisingly big underground explosion, but it probably offers the least in terms of sensual awareness. The reason for this is that if both parties are focussed on their own experience or 'black out' and become oblivious of each other, the sensation of the partner's orgasm is largely lost. For a woman, simultaneous orgasm is often followed by a feeling of disorientation, and a disappointment that lovemaking has come to such an abrupt end.

Though orgasm during intercourse is less acute, many of the women who are able to experience it prefer it for emotional reasons, because it involves complete body-to-body contact, holding the partner and giving oneself to him at the same time. 'Orgasm during intercourse is less intense, but it's more emotionally satisfying.' 'With penetration I feel more whole and loved.'

Feeling whole and loved and emotionally satisfied are important aspects of a good sexual relationship, but these feelings can be experienced whether orgasm takes place during intercourse or not. What is important is that women should experience regular clitoral orgasms. Orgasm relieves tension, recharges the body and revitalizes the mind. It leaves the woman feeling sparkling and whole. When shared with a partner, it represents the peak of sexual fulfilment and can be a powerful expression of love, helping to bring the couple closer together.

VAGINAL ACHE

The sensation of vaginal ache is experienced by many women at around the time they orgasm. It is like an intense longing in the vagina, an emptiness that desires to be filled. It is caused by the upper end of the vagina ballooning out, and most women experience it as a delicious urgency for penetration, though for some the feeling is hollow and painful. The pleasurable aching is usually not experienced if the penis is in the vagina at orgasm. Many women find that clitoral orgasm makes them desire intercourse strongly, and they enjoy penetration best immediately after orgasm.

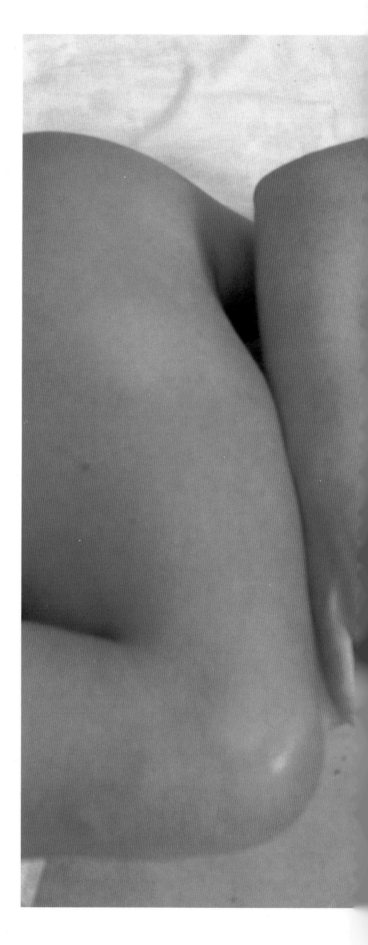

MULTIPLE AND SEQUENTIAL ORGASMS

The concept of multiple and sequential orgasms, like that of vaginal and clitoral orgasms, has caused a lot of confusion and left many women worried that their sexual response might be somehow inadequate. Because orgasms come in waves, some women are not even sure whether their orgasms are multiple or single. Multiple orgasms are those that are experienced in a chain, one directly after another; sequential orgasms are those with a gap of a few minutes between each one. It seems that true multiple orgasm is rare, although many women are capable of sequential orgasm.

Masters and Johnson wrote: 'If a female who is capable of having regular orgasms is properly stimulated within a short period after her first climax, she will in most instances be capable of having a second, third, fourth, and even a fifth and sixth orgasm before she is fully satiated. As contrasted with the male's usual inability to have more than one orgasm in a short period, many females, especially when clitorally stimulated, can regularly have five or six full orgasms within a matter of minutes.'

Being capable of six orgasms in a row is not the same as needing or even wanting that many. In fact, about 90 per cent of women who orgasm feel completely satisfied with a single climax. And in many women the clitoris remains hypersensitive, and further stimulation is uncomfortable or even painful. Those who do wish to go on find that a break of a few minutes is necessary after each orgasm for the focus of sensation and the desire for the next orgasm to return to the clitoris. However, some women who regularly give themselves several orgasms during masturbation feel inhibited about asking their partners to continue stimulating them for fear of appearing greedy or insatiable.

THE IMPORTANCE OF ORGASM TO GOOD SEX

Since the 1960s, when Kinsey began to bring sex out of the closet, there has been such a great deal of open discussion about the female orgasm that many women feel under intense pressure to 'perform'. If you feel your partner is comparing you to previous lovers, or to an orgasmic ideal in his head, it detracts from the intimate pleasure of sex and turns it into a competition.

Some women in Shere Hite's survey said they felt less than a 'real woman' if they didn't climax. One woman felt quite desperate: 'I must have an orgasm. Otherwise I'm not a real person and making him feel bad and maybe he'll abandon me.' Others claimed angrily that orgasm was their right. If men always had orgasms, why should *they* be denied? 'I *deserve* a climax after working him up to one. He has one so why shouldn't I? No matter how long it takes I make him rub my clitoris until I orgasm.'

It is easy to see why it might be difficult or impossible for a woman who feels pressured and self-conscious, frightened or angry to have an orgasm. Good sex derives from positive feelings, and stimulation to orgasm is not normally possible in an atmosphere of mutual mistrust.

Kinsey concluded that women *can* enjoy sex without orgasm, and marriages can survive without it if the couple place higher value on social and economic standing than on personal happiness. But he also recognized that if a woman persistently fails to reach orgasm, it does damage her relationship. Her reaction can be anything from disappointment with her own sexual response, leading to total lack of interest in sex, to pain, frustration, anger and resentment. Naturally, failure to satisfy his partner makes a caring man bewildered and hurt. One or both partners are likely to seek satisfaction elsewhere.

Women who never orgasm – about nine per cent, according to Shere Hite – felt that part of themselves was shut off. Only a couple of women were content with their non-orgasmic state; the rest felt bemused, unfulfilled in their relationships, jealous of women who could orgasm. Some gritted their teeth and said they would keep on trying until they died.

The best way to learn how to orgasm is to learn how to masturbate (see p. 86). Once you have mastered the technique, you can teach your partner – and it is never too late to learn.

INTIMACY

The best sex happens between lovers who are getting to know each other intimately, both physically and emotionally, as a result of an insatiable desire to explore each other's bodies and minds. No other activity gives such intense awareness of living in the present.

It is a sad fact that many couples have forgotten how to play. To them sex seems a serious business, and the various stages that need to be got through to reach the ultimate goal of orgasm are accomplished with efficiency. Sex becomes a habit, a ritual enacted without thought or enthusiasm. But sex is not about fulfilling a contract or proving yourself. It is not a duty or a competition, but an opportunity for sharing spontaneous excitement.

Creative sex is infinite in its variety, like improvisations on a theme. It can be playful, adventurous, erotic. It allows for many moods to express themselves one after another: passion, tenderness, lust, mischievous curiosity – whatever the lovers are feeling. An open approach to making love also allows other things to happen in bed besides sex: it encourages talk and laughter. In bed you can bare your soul as well as your body to your partner; you are also free to lose your inhibitions and just enjoy having fun together.

SHARING SEXUAL RESPONSIBILITY

With the advent of the Pill and the publication of the first studies into female sexuality in the 1960s, women entered an era of new sexual freedom. They realized their capacity for pleasure, and they discovered how to get it. Though men had been just as much in the dark as their partners, there was a tendency among some newly liberated women to blame them for their own lack of fulfilment in the past. A stereotype was born, of an insensitive man who cared only for his own sexual satisfaction, and who had intercourse without arousing his partner or bringing her to orgasm.

Although it is possible for a man to satisfy his own physical needs without giving either physical or emotional pleasure to his partner,

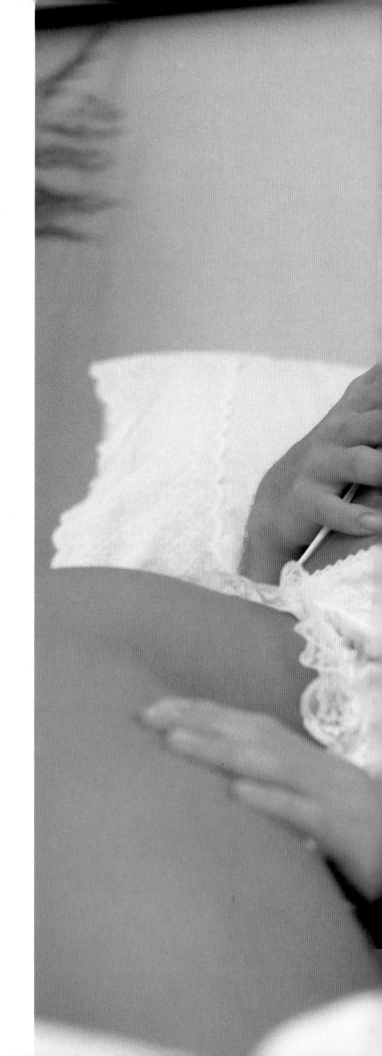

men today are far more aware that selfishness cripples relationships and means missing out on a whole spectrum of sexual sensation. So if your man doesn't satisfy you, don't dismiss him as insensitive when he may be just embarrassed or ignorant of the possibilities; show him what you enjoy and teach him how to do it for you.

Sharing sexual responsibility means being equal partners in making love. In the past it was considered 'fast' for women to take the initiative in sex, but good sex is sex without inhibitions, and that means not holding back when you want something. Being spontaneous, imaginative and inventive is part of the fun of making love, and both partners lose out if the woman regularly lies back and lets it 'be done' to her. Good sex is an engagement of minds and bodies: it happens when both partners participate to the full.

Another responsibility that should be shared is protection, against both pregnancy and disease. Don't always assume that a woman is on the Pill, or that she should automatically go on the Pill if you intend to form a relationship. Discuss which method of contraception will suit you both best, and always take a packet of condoms with you if it's your first time with a new partner. For more advice on contraception and protection against sexually transmitted diseases, see pp. 124 and 138.

UNDERSTANDING A MAN'S FEELINGS
All human beings are born sensitive, though men may appear to be less sensitive than women because they have been trained not to show their feelings. But tight self-control is an obstacle to intimacy. It often inhibits men in talking about their emotions and, particularly, about love. If you want to get closer, encourage your man to reveal how he feels, to express himself fully in actions and words, by showing and telling him the way you feel. He may need to be convinced that you will not think him 'less of a man' for admitting that he is subject to emotions beyond his control.

It is easy to underestimate a man's emotional vulnerability. But whether intercourse can take place or not depends solely on his ability to get and maintain an erection, and sometimes the pressure to 'perform' and the fear of failure can be overwhelming. This is particularly true of first-time sex (see p. 32). A woman can hide her lack of confidence, but in a man it's painfully obvious. The first thing a woman should understand is that if a man has a sexual problem it does not mean that he doesn't want you. If you assume this to be the case and respond with hurt and disappointment, you will only make him feel worse than he does already.

If he loses his erection or ejaculates prematurely, convince him that it's not that important and that you still want him by getting him to satisfy you with his fingers or his tongue. The knowledge that you don't just want him for his erect penis should restore some of his self-esteem, and arousing you and bringing you to orgasm may well renew his desire. For other advice on male problems, see p. 150.

Women also often underestimate men's genital sensitivity. The female sex organs are hidden and their response is complex and varies from one woman to the next. The male sex organs are prominent and comparatively mechanical in the way they function. But this does not mean that they are not also highly sensitive. Many women don't have the first idea about how to handle a penis. They grab and fumble, then give up.

However, some men like squeezing, some stroking, some rubbing; others like to feel the sensitive skin of the penis moving up and down over the whole length of the shaft, or at a particular point; some like fast movement, others slow; some vigorous, others gentle; some like the glans – the tip of the penis – to be stimulated, others not. And some like different things at different times. Some men like their testicles to be held or caressed; others are indifferent or too sensitive. Proceed tentatively, until you find out what feels good. Note his response, or ask him if you are not sure. Get him to show you how you could make it even better. For further information you should read the section on masturbation, p. 86.

UNDERSTANDING A WOMAN'S FEELINGS

For women, sex at its best involves total physical and emotional response. This is only possible if the feelings between you are positive and any discord or tensions have been resolved. Women love being aroused with kisses and caresses (see the section on Touching and closeness, p. 28). Their sexual response is individual and highly complex, and though most women are capable of orgasm, and need it for sexual fulfilment, you should not feel disappointed if your partner does not climax the first time you make love with her. It may take her a while to relax. Read the section on Female orgasm (p. 38), and proceed slowly and sensitively. Watch for her reactions, and ask her what she likes best.

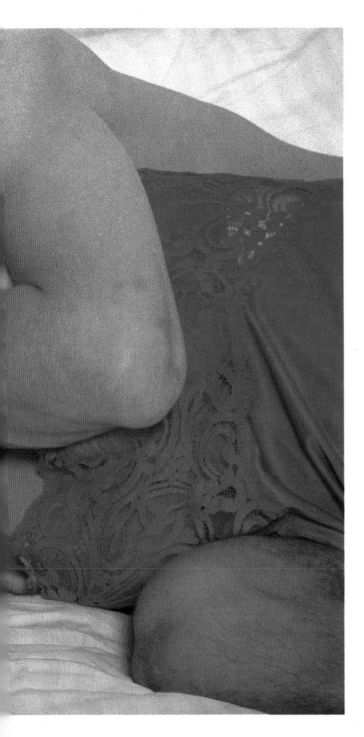

histrionics, and you can help her get in touch with her true feelings by making her feel accepted for what she is. You should keep an open mind, and encourage her to do the same, because there is not one 'standard' response that she should achieve.

Although only a minority of women orgasm during penetration, if you want to increase the chances of this, try the techniques of minimum entry and maximum withdrawal, which offer most stimulation to the vagina just below the clitoris. Support yourself with your arms on the bed for greater control. For minimum entry insert and withdraw just the tip of the penis; for maximum withdrawal push in slowly all the way, then pull out, straining against the top of the vagina, as far as you can without withdrawing completely, before pushing back in again.

Alternatively, one of you can stimulate the clitoris with your fingers while you are inside. Some women, however, find the dual stimulation makes it difficult to concentrate on the sensations experienced and therefore deadens the response.

Many women's sex drive is at its highest during menstruation, perhaps because there is no fear of conception. However, some are reticent to suggest making love then for fear that their menstrual blood will cause disgust. If your partner is holding back for this reason, either reassure her that blood does not bother you or suggest that she wears a diaphragm to hold back the flow, which may well be stimulated by sexual activity. It would be a great pity to deny her when she wants you so badly.

Finally, although women generally prefer long slow arousal to start with and closeness and tenderness afterwards, it would also be a great pity to deny your partner – and yourself – the immense excitement of sudden fast sex. Sensitive men tend to feel guilty about fulfilling overwhelming urges to have sex at odd times and in awkward places, but it gives a woman a unique thrill to be unexpectedly overtaken by desire when fully clothed and going about her daily business.

If your partner wishes very much to please you, but is not sure of her own sexual response, she may act out what she thinks she should be feeling by thrashing about and groaning. If you are well attuned, you should be able to tell if she is faking it. Encourage your partner to relax, be still and quiet and concentrate solely on the sensations you are giving her. Honesty and simplicity are what is needed in bed, and not

FANTASY

The imagination enriches life by offering alternatives to reality. Sexual fantasy offers immediate gratification of desire without the complication and responsibility of involving other people. It is a substitute for the sexual experience that we are prevented from indulging in, either because of practicalities, or because we are inhibited by social or cultural taboos.

Dreams are a rich and sometimes surprising outlet for the sexual impulse. The dramatist and critic Kenneth Tynan composed an imaginary letter on this subject to 'The Times': 'Dear Sir, I hope I am not a prude, but I feel compelled to lodge a protest against the ever-increasing flood of obscenity in dreams. Many of my friends have been as shocked and sickened as myself by the filth that is poured out nightly as soon as our eyes are closed. It is certainly not my idea of "home entertainment". Night after night, the most disgraceful scenes of perversion and bestiality are perpetrated behind my eyelids. . . . It is imperative that official action should be taken.'

Dreams, even more so than waking fantasies, are free of the jurisdiction of the internal censor who 'takes official action' and regulates our social behaviour. But whereas we have no control over our dreams, we can guide our fantasies.

A sexual fantasy will always differ from the real-life enactment of the very same scene in one important particular: in the fantasy everything can be controlled and runs in perfect accordance with the fantasizer's wishes. The will of the other person or people does not intrude, and nor do extraneous physical sensations. For this reason, sexual fantasy can form the perfect accompaniment to masturbation, with the fantasizer concentrating on marrying the fluid mental picture with the exquisite sensations of building up to orgasm.

SHARING YOUR FANTASIES
Private fantasy can also be used during intercourse as an aid to arousal and orgasm, and may prove an effective stimulus. The disadvantage is that it draws a veil between you and your partner and blocks out immediacy.

Instead of concentrating on what you are experiencing, you float off in your imagination to where you may be having sex with the man next door, or an anonymous stranger. The alienation from your partner and from the present is such that you might just as well be masturbating alone.

If you usually fantasize during intercourse, you are missing out. You can put your imagination to better use by talking to your partner about what sensations you enjoy the most, and showing him or her how to give them to you. Get your partner to proceed very slowly and gently, continuing to give guidance or encouragement. Concentrate together on every exquisite sensation, emptying your mind of all thought, giving your body over to pure feeling. An orgasm achieved this way is truly shared.

Some lovers go one step further and tell each other their private fantasies. In an atmosphere of complete trust and acceptance, this can be highly erotic. It can break down inhibitions and increase the intimacy of both minds and bodies. For couples who are less close, there is a risk. Hearing that your partner fantasizes about your best friend, or about someone at work, can make you angry and upset unless you are confident that there is no desire to turn fantasy into reality. Talking about your fantasy can also make you feel very vulnerable, because fantasies are a flimsy protection against reality, and they cover our weakest spots.

COMMON TYPES OF FANTASY AND WHAT THEY MEAN

The American author Nancy Friday has published three fat books full of fantasies sent to her by contributors from all over the United States. In *My Secret Garden* and *Forbidden Flowers* she quotes and comments on female fantasies; male fantasies are collected in *Men In Love*. Most commonly, for both men and women, fantasies involve simply imagining basic sexual activities with their lovers, with other people they know, or with one or more total strangers, real or anonymous. The settings may be exotic or unusual, the props and clothes

extravagant or bizarre, and the sexual prowess of the participants prodigious, but these features are just embellishments on a familiar theme.

The most common variations are fantasies that also involve elements of dominance and submission. Most people find something appealing in the idea of one partner being utterly at the tender mercy of the other. The submissive partner may be physically restrained in some way. This fantasy is probably so attractive because it recreates life's first loving experience of the mother ministering to the needs of the helpless baby. The passive partner relinquishes all responsibility, and is therefore 'permitted' to enjoy what happens in a totally selfish way; the active partner takes full control, and this role too offers selfish pleasure, albeit of a different sort.

Fantasies of dominance and submission deny the mutual participation of the one-to-one adult sex act and, in making the two roles opposite and distinct, free the participants from the responsibilities of closeness. These fantasies may be acted out by couples who are shy of intimacy, and the release brought by acknowledging the different needs of each partner may paradoxically bring the couple closer together.

Fantasies of slavery and bondage are variations on this theme. One of Shere Hite's male interviewees wrote: 'I always fantasize being the dominant. I would like to own a "slave" for sex purposes. Actually the feeling that someone cares enough to be my slave would be the most appealing thing about it.' This fantasy is interesting because it makes the passive person dominant. It reflects the total power of the 'helpless' infant to command its mother's full attention and be the focus of all her activity.

Another man wrote: 'I'm interested in both bondage and spanking occasionally. It is as much fun to be tied up as to be in control. I like the feeling of being tied up and subject to her will. I like mild spanking. We always leave the ropes loose . . . so when you want to get free fast and hug and cuddle, the ropes can be off in a flash. It's the fantasy of being subject to

someone's will that's the turn-on.' Even though this man acted out his fantasy with his partner, the ropes were only loosely tied and the spanking was mild. The turn-on remained because the couple were play-acting, holding the fantasy still in their minds.

But why should anyone find spanking appealing? Again the answer lies in early childhood. A child who has been spanked for playing with his or her genitals will associate genital arousal with an admonitory whack on the bottom. In time, the two sensations may become inseparable, and there are some people who find it impossible to orgasm without the stimulation of being spanked. The reason this happens more often to men than to women is that little boys' genitals are more accessible, and so they are more likely to fiddle with themselves and be caught doing so than little girls.

However, for people like the man quoted above who enjoy it occasionally, spanking is not a problem. The very word 'spank' shows that this game is associated with the feeling that sex is 'naughty'. Spanking, bondage and slavery are harmless ways of gaining sexual pleasure for those who wish to escape from the responsibility of the adult relationship into the irresponsibility of childhood.

Leather is associated with bondage, hence its thrill; other fabrics also appeal to the sexual imagination. The fabric forms a barrier between the lover and the loved one's body, and this has the tantalizing effect of heightening desire, while at the same time offering protection against the demands of naked intimacy.

Silk is valued for its smoothness, and its transparency when wet; fur for its resemblance to pubic hair; and rubber for its ability to cling to the figure. When wet, the feel of rubber resembles that of the body's inner skin.

FANTASIES INVOLVING VIOLENCE
Most of Shere Hite's interviewees had not experimented in real life with any of their fantasies of domination and submission, bondage, slavery or spanking, and were not interested in trying them out. The idea of

translating fantasies of violence into reality was generally found repellant. 'Hurting someone even if it thrills them ain't sex to me,' wrote one man. 'Sex is tenderness and softness. The thought of inflicting pain during sex, or for that matter any time, is obnoxious to me.' Nevertheless, many men did enjoy fantasies of rape, though they invariably ended with the 'victim' participating fully and enjoying herself.

Shere Hite suggests that male fantasies of violence and rape reflect a massive frustration with the lack of meaningful and close relationships. Failure to establish intimacy by normal interaction can trigger the desire to 'smash and grab' for it, to batter down the barriers and snatch the prize. The reward for violence is that the man is able to share pleasure with his partner. The implication is that he lacks the confidence to believe that his partner could completely desire him in reality.

Her study of male rape fantasies leads Shere Hite to the conclusion that men do not rape in real life out of lust – they can achieve orgasm easily through masturbation – but out of anger with women, and out of a lack of self-esteem. When love is thwarted, it comes out as violence.

In Western patriarchal society, masculinity is equated with dominance. Men are supposed to 'take' women (both in the sense of 'taking a bride', and sexually). It is a man's 'right' to take and a woman's 'duty' to yield. If a woman rejects a man, she is therefore 'denying him his rights'. He therefore has every 'right' to take what he wants by force. Many men who continue to feel that they have rights over women's bodies see taking them – raping them – as a symbol of personal acceptance and masculine status.

Shere Hite writes: 'The more a man lacks self-esteem, the more he may attempt to make the physical act of sex a substitute for emotional contact, and the more a man finds this is the only way he is able to relate in a personal, emotional way to others, the more likely he is to complain that he doesn't get enough sex. These thought patterns can eventually lead some men to the feeling that they are completely justified in raping a woman.'

MARRIAGE AND INFIDELITY

Marriage is 'an honorable estate', the cornerstone of the family unit upon which our culture is built. It provides domestic comfort, financial security and social respectability. It can also be perceived as a trap by some people. By prescribing certain duties and responsibilities and curtailing the freedom of the individual, it transforms a love affair into a legally binding commitment with a promise of a lifetime's fidelity. As Groucho Marx once said: 'Marriage is a great institution. But who wants to live in an institution?' His comment reflects the ambiguity that many people feel about monogamy.

There is a common feeling among the majority of both men and women that marriage kills sex. People don't get tired of sex, and can lead fulfilling and active sex lives well into old age; but they do, it appears, get tired of sex with the same partner year after year. A recent survey revealed that 70 per cent of married people have had extramarital sex. The most frequent reason given for this was that sex within marriage was either boring, minimal, or non-existent. Why should this be so?

WHY CAN MARRIED SEX BE BORING?

Good sex happens between people who are intensely aware of each other's minds and bodies, and alive to each other's feelings. But in most marriages the intimacy needed for good sex wanes with time as the framework of wedlock imposes itself and the partners fit into the traditional roles demanded by society.

As Women's Lib pointed out twenty years ago, these roles are unequal and outdated. They evolved when we developed from hunter-gatherers into being meat-eaters (see p.18). They give men superior status in society: that of

money-earners, property-owners and decision makers; whereas women are active mainly in the background, as home-makers and child-minders. The sexes are born equal, and although society is becoming increasingly aware that there is no longer a reason why they should not also grow up equal, thousands of years of conditioning are hard to break.

The problem with imposing unequal roles on equal partners is that it causes resentment on both sides. Social conditioning forces this resentment underground, and for the most part it is unacknowledged, but it is still there. Women cannot help but feel resentment at becoming 'second-class citizens'; men cannot help but feel resentment at women's dependence on them. Both feel that they have been trapped by the other into becoming housewives and mothers on the one side, and providers and protectors on the other.

Because women take on the roles of cooking, cleaning and caring for their husbands, men often come to view their wives in the same light as they viewed their mothers; many men even call their wives 'mother'! Since mothers are always seen as 'sexless', 'good women', men whose wives perform motherly duties come to regard them without lust. Just as it would be 'wrong' to lust after your mother, unless you were some kind of pervert, it becomes unacceptable to lust after your wife. Sex in the marital bed becomes sex without passion: a rather pedestrian affair.

Spontaneity and delight dwindle from the bedtime relationship. As the partners settle into their allotted roles, the average marriage comes to resemble a successful and friendly small business rather than a love affair.

EXTRAMARITAL AFFAIRS
People have extramarital affairs because intimacy, eroticism and adventure have gone from their marriages. For the most part, they do not tell their partners, for fear of guilt and recrimination rocking the boat, and possibly breaking up the marriage. Affairs are sallies into the outside world of freedom, where married

men and women can prove to themselves their sexual potency and desirability, and enjoy a secret act of revenge on their partner, with whom they no longer feel either potent or desirable.

Sometimes, of course, a string of affairs leads to the realization that so much is lacking in the marriage that it is unsalvageable, but most extramarital affairs do not pose a real threat to the institution. They are 'escapades' which are hidden from the spouse in much the same way as naughtiness would be hidden from a disapproving parent. Some people use affairs to 'keep themselves going' in a marriage that has worn thin, but whose commitments seem inescapable; others see their extramarital experience simply as selfish enrichment of their own lives – a token 'independence'.

The attraction of an affair is that it holds the promise of an experience that is the exact opposite of marriage. There are no social responsibilities to cripple the lovers' attitudes to one another or inhibit their sexuality; and the limited time available for encounters heightens emotional urgency. In this atmosphere, intimacy and good sex thrive.

Occasionally, and particularly in a marriage in which one partner has outgrown the other, an extramarital affair develops into a full and passionate relationship which has far more emotional significance than the marriage itself. Yet the chances are that even this may not break up the marriage because social conditioning places the utmost importance on preserving respectability and the status quo, and the guilt involved in destroying these would be insupportable. It is a case of 'Love does not conquer all', as in the end, many people prefer security to upheaval, whatever the price they have to pay in personal suffering.

NURTURING INTIMACY
If intimacy is a prerequisite for good sex, and marriage with its stereotyped roles kills intimacy with a good dose of resentment, should married couples give up hope of a lifetime of good sex? The answer, of course, is 'No'.

The first thing an engaged couple should do is to ask themselves whether they really want to formalize their union. After all, the natural thing might be to see this relationship develop as one in a series of fulfilling partnerships. Human pair-bonding was originally life-long because that was the time it took to bring up an infant. Today, when life expectancy is around three-quarters of a century, that biological imperative is obviously redundant, and more people are contemplating alternatives to traditional marriage.

Most people get married because of social pressure to do so. When questioned why they had got married in the first place, a group of men mostly gave answers along the lines of: 'I don't know – because it was the thing to do', and 'Because everybody does it'. Only a very few said that they had got married because of their interest in, liking for or love of their specific partner. If 'being married' is more important than your desire to explore the potential of your relationship, then you are starting off with very low expectations of intimacy indeed.

In order to nurture intimacy, men and women need to question the validity of the traditional married roles to their lives, and choose the role and the relationship best suited to their individual needs. If the responsibilities of each partner are fully discussed and agreed upon, and regularly reviewed, instead of being taken for granted, there is less chance that resentment will develop. Frequent open discussion of this and every other aspect of the relationship is what will break down the barriers between you, thereby creating deeper understanding and bringing you closer together.

Being open about your feelings, physical and emotional, is crucial to keeping intimacy alive. Of course, absolute honesty with your partner carries the risk of rejection, but it is a risk worth taking from the start if it secures complete trust between you. The best sex, and the most uninhibited sex, takes place in an atmosphere of unreserved mutual trust, knowledge and acceptance, and, as intimacy grows, so sex gets better and better all the time.

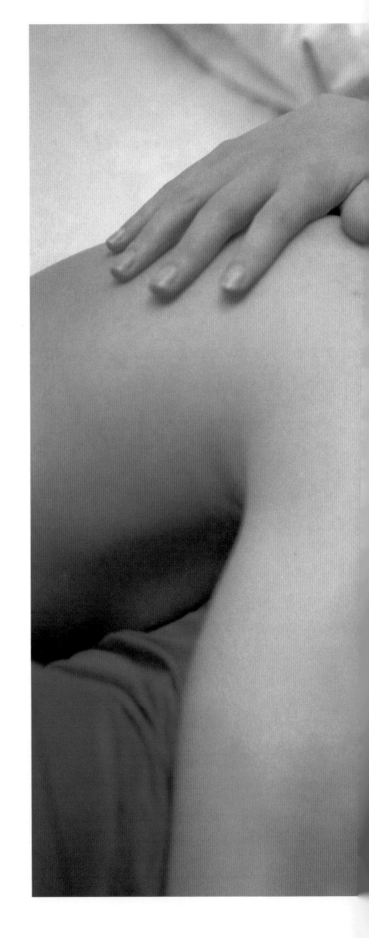

EXPERIMENTAL SEX

Sex for the sake of it, without love or involvement, is often experimented with by men and women as part of their quest for real fulfilment. People who boast about their experiences with prostitutes and about swinging and swapping are keen to convey that these are 'advanced' sex practices, in some way better or more exciting than the 'real thing', although anyone who has experienced both will acknowledge that they are just a substitute for good close one-to-one sex. Experiments are usually indulged in out of boredom or desperation, or because of an inability to face the responsibility of mutual emotional involvement (for more information see p.65).

But boredom and desperation are felt by most people at some stage in their lives, and many are as curious to experiment with their sexuality as they are to discover their potential and learn their likes and dislikes in other areas.

The risks that go with sexual experimentation are high. The more sexual partners you have, the greater the chance of catching VD and AIDS (see pp.136 and 138); for protection, men and women intent on experiment should always carry a packet of condoms. The emotional risks are not negligible either, and such encounters may often leave you feeling degraded and worthless, especially if you are a woman. Other consequences of licentious sexual behaviour are not immediately apparent.

CREATIVITY AND THE SEXUAL URGE

Freud put forward the theory that indiscriminate sexual activity used up the creative urge, which could otherwise be put to use for the benefit of society as a whole. His theory was borne out by J. D. Unwin, who examined various societies across the world, present and past, and found that those that practised monogamy and censured sex outside of it were more advanced than permissive societies. For example, the Victorians, who were extremely sexually repressed, diverted their energies into empire-building, and transformed the towns and cities of Britain. The South Sea Islanders, on the other hand, led a life of totally open and uncensured promiscuity, but were economically and culturally naïve. The Roman Empire, which had been built on strict discipline and order, eventually collapsed amidst scenes of orgiastic debauchery.

For the individual, as well as for society, there is a choice. A life given over to indiscriminate sex makes achievements in other areas impossible. The less drive you dissipate in sex, the more you will have for other activities. And while it is generally believed that a person who is sexually fulfilled in a strong relationship is better able to function than one who is repressed or thwarted, sexual self-restraint, and even periods of celibacy in between relationships, do not necessarily lead to frustration. Indeed, these can prove to be the most creative periods in an individual's life, when the output of work and new ideas is at its peak. Most people will have experienced periods at the beginning and end of a relationship, which are turbulent times emotionally and sexually, when they have been unable to concentrate on anything; likewise, once the grief after a break-up has finally faded, there is often a burst of intense creative activity and achievement.

PAYING FOR SEX

Prostitutes, the members of the world's so-called 'oldest profession', have been the butt of man's hatred for woman since time immemorial. The history of prostitution in Britain makes grim reading. Until the widespread use of the condom in the 1860s and '70s, prostitutes were regularly infected by their clients with syphilis and other venereal diseases, which they in turn passed on. They lived in increasing filth and degradation, often dying insane or blind after suffering terrible agonies, with alcohol as their only comfort. They were preached at by moralizing zealots, who were ignorant of the poverty and desperation that had turned them to the streets; and they were subject to brutal treatment: compulsory incarceration and examination by officers of the law, often under the eyes of jeering crowds. It has been suggested that the murders of Jack the Ripper were an act of revenge by a man who had contracted VD from a whore; this was certainly the motive of at least two other multiple murderers whose targets were prostitutes.

The lives of today's prostitutes have benefited immeasurably from the advances in the prevention and cure of venereal disease. The profession thrives on clients who have an otherwise less than adequate sexual outlet, sometimes because the type of sexual gratification they crave is available nowhere else. Some prostitutes specialize in catering for men with sexual inhibitions that make them turn to sadism (in which sexual pleasure is gained from cruelty or abuse to another; named after the French writer, the Marquis de Sade, 1740-1814) or masochism (sexual pleasure gained from being physically abused; named after the Austrian novelist Leopold von Sacher-Masoch, 1835-95). Indeed, prostitutes can command a high price for allowing such men to enact their fantasies.

Other men visit prostitutes for quick sexual relief either because they do not want to be bothered with the process of getting to know someone, which would cost both time and money, or because they are unable to form relationships. Sometimes adolescent boys visit a prostitute, either alone or goaded on by their mates, for their first sexual experience. In all cases, paying for sex has the advantage of being secret, anonymous, quick, free of the fear of rejection, and without any of the pressures of social or emotional involvement.

Of the men Kinsey interviewed, 69 per cent had had sex with a prostitute at one time or another, and most were disappointed for the same reason as Shere Hite's interviewees, whose main reaction was that having to pay made them feel they were personally undesirable and therefore less masculine. They disliked the fact that it was just a business transaction, and that the prostitute showed them no warmth or affection and took no pleasure herself. Many felt degraded by the impersonality of the encounter, although this was exactly what others valued, regarding it as just another professional service.

SWINGING AND SWAPPING

These are the terms used for experiments in which couples exchange partners, either within a group or within a foursome, and have sex, often in each other's presence. This type of sexual diversion was particularly popular among bored Americans before the advent of AIDS, and swingers' clubs, with bars, swimming pools, jacuzzis, saunas and large and small rooms full of mattresses, operated quite openly.

The health risk aside, swingers face grave emotional danger. Belonging and possessing are inescapable elements of sexual love, and people who claim not to be jealous are almost invariably kidding themselves. It can be a very destructive experience to witness your partner apparently enjoying sex with someone else, especially as the reason for swinging in the first place has to be that sex between you is pretty mediocre. The worst possible situation occurs when one of the partners is reluctant, and has gone along just to please the other in the hope of avoiding secret infidelity. Sex with people you don't know or care about can seem pointless and squalid, and sex with other couples whom you know and like can ruin friendships. To perform publicly an act that is naturally private can be sordid and degrading.

The aim of swinging is to introduce variety into a stale marriage, and by giving your partner permission to have sex with others under your supervision, to grant him or her a new measure of 'independence', while, at the same time, banishing jealousy. The same idea was behind the communes of the 1960s and '70s, which espoused 'free love' and 'open marriage'. Many of these communes disbanded, the relationships within them broken up by jealousy and guilt.

Psychiatrists who have studied open marriages and swinging partnerships report that tragic complications inevitably arise and lead to the ultimate breakdown of the relationship, which is usually entering its final phase when the experiments take place. If we lived like South Sea Islanders, no doubt we could share our partners without disastrous consequences, but the truth is that we don't and we can't.

HOMOSEXUALITY

Human sexuality is a complex phenomenon, and not so neatly categorized by the labels 'heterosexual' and 'homosexual' as society could wish. Between the strong and exclusive attraction of man to woman, and that of man to man, or woman to woman, lies a whole spectrum of sexual and emotional affinities: the ardour, or warmth, or coolness of any human relationship depends on the individuals within it, and not on any of the arbitrary specifications which might be imposed by society.

Some men want sex with other men as a permanent part of their lives; some are curious about male bodies, and may experiment at some time in their lives; some feel equally attracted to men and to women; some men enjoy looking at other men's bodies without desiring sexual contact; some prefer the company of other men for leisure; some work in an all-male environment. Women also feel and do all these things with other women.

These infinite permutations and the confusion that results from them cannot be accommodated by society, which needs order in which to function. Order means ignoring varying shades of grey and distinguishing only between black and white; it means putting labels on things. And since society is never stronger than when it is united against a common evil, labelling things also means defining society's outcasts.

According to Kinsey, in our culture, homosexuals first became outcasts in the seventh century BC, when the Jews returned from exile in Babylon. Until then, homosexual activity had been associated with the Jewish religious service, as it had been with the religious services of most of the other peoples of Asia. But the Jews were now experiencing a wave of nationalism, and in order to create for themselves a distinct identity, they decided to break with many of the customs they had shared with their neighbours. Henceforth, homosexuality was condemned as pagon idolatry. Later it became a matter of morals, and finally a question of criminality.

Homosexuality was criminalized in Great Britain in 1885, 16 years after the term was first coined. Prior to that, it was not recognized as a state of being, and men who had sex with other men were persecuted only fitfully; indeed, in Britain there was an unspoken acknowledgement that under certain conditions, for example at boys' schools, at universities, between master and valet, and in other all-male environments, sexual relations between men were not unnatural.

It took 82 years of repression before the Act forbidding homosexual practices was repealed in 1967, years in which men might be thought 'suspect' if they expressed any of the gentler emotions, such as sensitivity, caring or creativity. Ironically, the publicity that surrounded the repeal of the Act served only to exacerbate hostility towards practising homosexuals; and in recent years the AIDS epidemic (see p.136) has again stirred up hatred towards them. In his book 'Sex, Death and Punishment', Richard Davenport-Hines quotes an 89-year-old grandmother who told the 'Daily Express' in 1986: 'The homosexuals who have brought this plague upon us should be locked up. Burning is too good for them. Bury them in a pit and pour on quick-lime . . .'

THE SHOCK OF THE KINSEY REPORT

When Alfred Kinsey published his report *Sexual Behaviour in the Human Male* in 1948, the Home Office considered prosecution on grounds of obscenity. Of all his findings, the one that provoked the most vehement outcry was the revelation that homosexual behaviour was not a minority aberration, but that one man in three had had some form of homosexual experience resulting in orgasm. Kinsey was not saying that one man in three was homosexual; but he was tearing off the label that branded sexuality between men as 'abnormal'. People who thought they could recognize a homosexual when they saw one – the stereotype was an effete and weedy specimen, usually an artist or an aristocrat – were terrified to discover that homosexuality was confined by neither class, nor education, nor appearance. Among the most terrified were men whose fear of their own

gay tendencies had led them to speak out in the forefront of the battle against gays.

In addition to the 37 per cent who had reached orgasm with another male, a further 23 per cent of Kinsey's male interviewees had had homosexual experience that had fallen short of orgasm, and another 16 per cent admitted erotic attraction to other men that they had done nothing about. The incidence of active homosexuality was 27 per cent at age 15, rose in the late teens to 33 per cent, fell between the ages of 21 and 25, and then rose again among unmarried men to 39 per cent between the ages of 36 and 40. Kinsey put the fall in the early 20s down to the fact that most men got married at this age, and he explained the rise in the mid-life age group by saying that those men who had tried to conform and failed, later turned back to homosexuality.

Kinsey pointed out that humans were not alone among animals in engaging in same-sex activity: the assumption that animals had sex only when reproduction could be guaranteed was a man-made one, designed to bolster the view that homosexuality was 'against nature'.

Of course, four decades have elapsed since the publication of the Kinsey Report and sexual mores and attitudes towards sex have changed, particularly since the 1960s, which ushered in a more permissive and tolerant view of sex. However, Kinsey's findings still represent extremely valuable research into this area of sexual behaviour and the underlying trends are still relevant today.

WHY ARE SOME MEN HOMOSEXUAL?

Various attempts have been made this century to 'explain' homosexuality, and even to 'cure' it. Opinion was divided as to whether homosexuality was a physical or a psychological condition. One theory proposed that homosexuality was transmitted in a defective gene passed on by elderly parents, another that it was due to lesions or malfunctions in the brain. Painful and debilitating electric shock treatment was given to homosexuals as a 'cure' without any effect on their sexuality. When the sex hormones were discovered in the 1930s, it was thought that homosexuals probably suffered a hormonal imbalance; but although injections of the male hormone testosterone had an excitant effect, they did nothing to make homosexuals heterosexual.

Freud's theories centred on the relationship between the male infant and his parents. He believed that there were several factors that could encourage a boy to grow up incapable of relating sexually to women. If he was smothered and completely dominated by his mother, he might grow up afraid of and repelled by women. On the other hand, if he was intimidated and harshly treated by his father, he might later look for a loving male partner with whom to resolve the unsatisfactory relationship.

All these theories pointed to the fact that the homosexual was a damaged person – either physically defective or psychologically stunted – and contributed considerably to the image of the homosexual as a social outcast. However, behavioural science has since shed new light on human sexuality, and these humiliating theories have largely been rejected. It now seems certain that the natural condition of the human being at birth is *sexuality*, and that whether this sexuality is orientated more towards the opposite sex or the same sex depends very largely on the prevailing code of the society in which the child is brought up.

The Ancient Greeks practised homosexuality; so did the early Hebrews. In some South American tribes today, homosexuality is the norm and heterosexual intercourse takes place only on ceremonial occasions for the purpose of procreation. In some parts of North Africa and among some American Indians, homosexuality plays a large part in communal life. People born into a homosexual society generally conform to the norm, just as do people born into a heterosexual society. Most of us have a broad enough sexual response to allow us to be conditioned comfortably to either mode of behaviour. The people who feel less comfortable with the status quo, and those who feel positive discomfort with

it are in no way unnatural; rather, it is the restrictions that society places on them that should be considered against nature.

The question is not really why some people are homosexual, but why our society is heterosexual. As more people question and explore their own sexual responses, and discover that they are not always as black and white as they had thought, so there will be more tolerance towards sexuality as a whole. With increased tolerance, there will be more scope for expression of individual sexuality, and when this happens, society will be on the way to liberty and equality for all.

HOW MEN RELATE SEXUALLY TO EACH OTHER

More than 40 years after the publication of the Kinsey Report, which demonstrated that homosexuality was both high in incidence and entirely natural, prejudice remains. Among people like the 89-year-old grandmother quoted on p.68, homosexuals are frequently openly loathed and feared. Much of this hostility comes from ignorance, and from ignorance of one's own complex sexuality as much as anything else. So how do male lovers behave towards one another?

Eleven per cent of the men who answered Shere Hite's questionnaires said that they preferred sex with men. They described their sexual encounters as beginning in foreplay and ending in orgasm, but the pattern of their lovemaking was much less rigid than the pattern of lovemaking between men and women tends to be, and the other difference was that both partners almost always reached orgasm.

'With my male lover,' wrote one man in a fairly typical reply, 'our sex consists of a lot of conversation; affectionate kissing, holding; body contact – a great deal of oral exchanges – deep tongue kissing – tongue in ears, on neck – and all over body – use of tongue, lips on penis – and hands all over the body – massaging – masturbating – lotion lubrication – on penis and hands – usually ending in anal sex – mutual – or quite often 69.'

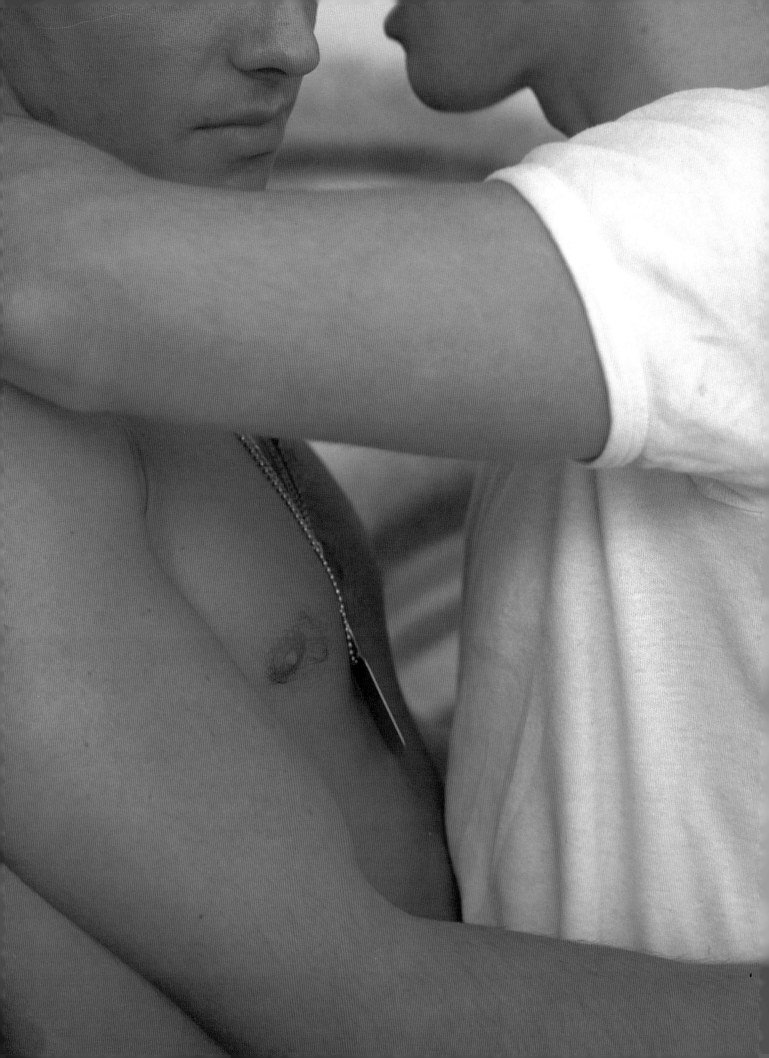

Sex with other men was considered by many to be liberating because there were no rules: it did not involve pressure to perform or pressure to satisfy the other person, and mutual satisfaction was effortless because men understood each other's bodies so well. 'How is sex with men different from sex with women? Generally I think men know exactly what physical stimulation works for each other. You do for someone else what you know you enjoy.'

Many men described exuberant feelings on holding, hugging and kissing their male partners, and emphasized that their lack of inhibition in expressing physical affection with a man stemmed from a feeling of equality that those who had tried it had not found in their relationships with women. One man wrote: 'Society expects me to be dominant in my work, in social affairs, in my spirituality (*vis-à-vis* the Catholic idea of male supremacy), and also in my home life including bed. That is *too damn much* dominancy. I need to be able to feel "catered to" emotionally at times too. Thus, I find a homosexual relationship much more rewarding in that I can have a healthy balance . . .' The sense of freedom and relief that sex with a man did not carry the social obligations that surrounded sex with a woman was widely felt: 'You don't have to worry about having to support her, or marry her.'

Another advantage of sex without obligations was that men felt they could come straight to the point: a sexual relationship often preceded a social friendship, and not the other way around. Many men described their sexual relations with male partners as generally more honest and straightforward, both physically and emotionally, than their relationships with women had been.

On the question of promiscuity, the feeling was that gay men were no more inherently promiscuous than straight men, and that promiscuity had nothing to do with sexual preference. Some were promiscuous, but for most the ideal was one lasting relationship freely entered into, i.e. with no rigid commitment to monogamy from either partner.

ANAL PENETRATION

It is not only homosexual men who enjoy anal penetration. Thirty-one per cent of all the men questioned by Shere Hite had tried anal penetration with a finger – their own or a partner's – and a further 12 per cent had tried it with a penis or a penis-sized object. Of the men who considered themselves homosexual, 86 per cent had tried anal penetration with a penis, though most said it was not something they did daily, unlike finger-penetration, which could be practised even during masturbation. Almost all the men who had tried anal penetration said they liked it. (For information on anal penetration of women, see p.93.)

Most of the men who had tried it derived a great deal of physical and emotional satisfaction from being penetrated. To be penetrated, to let someone in to your body, is a very different kind of experience from penetrating: it requires openness, trust, and a recognition of vulnerability. The sensation of being 'filled' by another man's penis gave many men a feeling of being made complete. Another reason why anal stimulation should be so pleasurable is that the male prostate gland is situated within a couple of inches inside the back passage and can be felt by pressing a finger at this point slightly downwards and to the front of the body. Stimulation of the prostate gland can cause orgasm, although most men also need penile stimulation.

As the anal sphyncter is a tight, ring-like opening, care needs to be taken not to penetrate it too quickly. A gentle easing-in is best and, as the muscles relax, thrusts can be longer and deeper. Hygiene should always be the first priority in any act of anal penetration, as disease is especially easily transmitted in this way. Always wear a condom. A condom on a finger inserted into the anus can aid lubrication as well as protect against scratches – from fingernails and rough skin – that could lead to infection. You should always wash thoroughly before and after anal sex, and if you use a vibrator for penetration, make sure that this is washed thoroughly too, in hot soapy water with a splash of antiseptic added.

WHY AREN'T MORE WOMEN LESBIANS?

Although society allows women to be much more demonstrative in showing their affection towards one another than men, Kinsey found that fewer women had had homosexual experiences. Only 28 per cent of the women in his survey admitted to erotic feelings for other women, and only 13 per cent had followed these experiences through to have sexual contact resulting in orgasm. Yet those who had had sex with women generally found it much more satisfying than sex with men. Kinsey found that after five years of marriage, 40 per cent of women reach orgasm nine out of ten times with their partners, whereas among lesbian couples, 68 per cent achieve regular orgasm. The implication is that women make better sexual partners for women than men do!

Why then are there relatively few lesbians about? First of all, many more women may have had homosexual experiences than Kinsey's survey suggests, but may not wish to admit it. However, women may also find it difficult to give and interpret sexual signals among themselves. In a man, an erection is a sign of sexual arousal that cannot be missed or misinterpreted, but a woman has no such obvious equivalent. Her desire communicates itself physically in her eyes, her voice, and the attitude of her body, but if she is unsure how the other woman will react, her signals will be more subtle, and may be taken for nothing more than friendship. Unless one of the pair risks giving out an explicit signal, the attraction may never be recognized.

It is probably true to say that many women do not realize that the erotic attraction they feel is mutual. Shere Hite was struck by the number of women answering her questionnaires who said, when asked what kind of sexual experience they would like but had not tried, that they wanted to have sex with another woman. Part of the problem is of course that women are conditioned by society and upbringing to be pursued in love and not to do the pursuing themselves, and this makes their reticence all the more natural.

THE LESBIAN RELATIONSHIP

Lesbianism is as natural among animals as is male homosexuality. Kinsey reported that lesbian sex had been observed among rats, mice, hamsters, guinea pigs, rabbits, porcupines, martens, cattle, antelope, goats, horses, pigs, sheep, lions, monkeys and chimpanzees. Women, like men, are born 'sexual' and may find satisfaction with either sex, but they usually allow themselves to be conditioned by society to prefer one sex and shun the other. Some women rebel against the narrowness of the status quo and become lesbians for political reasons, feeling dissatisfied with a male-dominated society; others do so because they find men unsatisfactory as lovers or as partners on an emotional level; and others because they are intensely emotionally involved with a member of their own sex and wish to express their feelings through their sexuality.

Women describe sex with each other as a seamless experience, beginning more gently and lasting longer than sex with men. Like male homosexuals, lesbians tend to experience more imaginative and varied sex than they had heterosexually: there is no set 'menu' to follow, goal to aim for or roles to adopt. One woman in Shere Hite's survey said that making love with her female partner was a circular process that did not stop automatically when one of them had an orgasm. Another woman wrote: 'With women there is a lot of hugging, kissing, caressing, i.e. a lot more touching and affection. There is not any particular procedure, only there is usually either finger-clitoral stimulation or cunnilingus to produce orgasm at some point. Women are warmer, more mutual, careful to see how I'm reacting, as opposed to most men, and sex is slower. Women consider the whole body erotic since there is no one concentrated "tool" for pleasure.'

It appears that heterosexuals have a lot to learn from homosexuals of both sexes, in attitude towards their sexual relationships, in technique and in the shedding of the inhibitions that can so easily cripple the free expression of human sexuality.

BISEXUALITY
Some people manage to retain their original sexual ambivalence and remain attracted to both sexes in adulthood. Bisexuality is a remarkable achievement. Whereas both heterosexuals and homosexuals have made a firm decision in favour of one sex, and many tend to find the idea of intimate contact with the other sex repellant, the bisexual is capable of enjoying both. To be bisexual means having the freedom to explore one's own sexual responses to the full and to acknowledge a more complex sexuality than many would dare to contemplate. However, bisexuality does carry a greater risk of AIDS than heterosexuality.

Bisexuality can take many forms. Some bisexuals find that they establish a pattern in

TRANSVESTISM

A transvestite is a man who 'cross-dresses' in women's clothes. Transvestites are not necessarily homosexuals, nor do they necessarily need to wear female clothes for sex. Cross-dressing is not easily understood, but may have its roots in the man's childhood, in an emotional dependence associated with items of his mother's clothing. Many male transvestites were dressed as girls when they were small.

Married men who are transvestites often try to hide the fact from their wives, fearing that discovery might cause a breakdown of the relationship, although, as dressing-up is harmless, some women are able to cope well with this behaviour. A transvestite who is distressed by his need to dress up will probably find that psychotherapy helps.

TRANSSEXUALITY

Transsexuals are people who feel that they were born into the wrong sex. They are unhappy with their bodies and try, through hormone therapy and surgery, to change their sex. Transsexuals have often been dressed and treated as members of the opposite sex when small, and their problem is one of mistaken gender identity. They may or may not be homosexual.

Transsexuality is a very distressing condition that causes a great deal of misery and confusion to sufferers and their families. To spare the transsexual the emotional and physical agony of a sex change in adulthood, many male and female transsexuals are now given therapy to resolve their gender problem before they reach puberty. If this does not happen, the transsexual may become depressed and suicidal unless a sex change is granted. This involves surgery to construct a vagina in a man, or enlarge the clitoris in a woman. Female transsexuals take male hormones to promote the growth of facial hair and make the voice break, and males take female hormones to make their breasts develop. The whole process is lengthy and the patient must be supported by professional counselling. There is no guarantee of a satisfactory sex life after surgery has taken place.

which heterosexual relationships alternate with homosexual relationships. Some married bisexuals find that whereas an affair with a member of the opposite sex might jeopardize their long-term relationship, a homosexual affair can be tolerated by the other partner. Because it is not seen as a threat, it can actually help to keep the marriage together.

And for some bisexuals the answer is to live in a triangle of three lovers, two women and a man, or two men and a woman, where each accepts the dual claims and attractions of the others. This arrangement, called troilism (from the French word 'trois', meaning 'three'), has erotic appeal for a large number of people who might enjoy the sexual experience without wanting to make it a permanent set-up.

Erotic Technique

Passionate sex between lovers can be made even more exciting by the cultivation of erotic technique. Exploring your own and your partner's responses is a sexual adventure that opens the way to a deeper and more thrilling level of intimacy.

THE CULTIVATION OF EROTIC TECHNIQUE

Since the 1960s, which saw the widespread use of the Pill and the beginning of female emancipation, sex has gradually ceased to be a taboo subject. The Pill gave women the freedom to explore their sexuality, and to take initiative and responsibility where traditionally they were restricted to a passive role. As they moved towards equality, women claimed their natural right to sexual pleasure and put their relationship with men under public scrutiny. The whole subject of sex was opened up, with both men and women eager to learn its secrets, acknowledging that there was not just one way to have sex, and that variations and refinements could bring increased pleasure. Sex manuals were published, and became best sellers.

Of course, the sex manuals of the '60s were not the first to be written. The most famous of all, the 'Kama Sutra', was written in the first century AD. This book is now available in paperback, but it has little relevance to life in the 1990s, and many of the famously erotic positions it describes can be achieved only by those who are highly experienced in advanced yoga techniques. Sex manuals are as much mirrors of social attitudes as they are instruction books, and that is why they will continue to be written and revised.

THEORY AND PRACTICE

People buy sex books for two basic reasons: to confirm to themselves that they are like other people, that they have problems that are not insoluble and desires that are not abnormal and can be fulfilled; and out of a sense of curiosity and adventure, in search of new ideas and new ways of arousing and satisfying themselves and their partners. This middle section of the book is about arousal and satisfaction.

It goes without saying that sexual desire and fulfilment cannot be learned from a book. You can't will yourself to fall in love with someone or

to want that person: these things happen spontaneously. (Indeed, they often happen against your will and better judgement!) And no amount of finesse in lovemaking techniques will bring fire to a relationship that is at best lukewarm. Erotic technique is really only useful to stoke up the fires of an already hot relationship, or to cause one that is smouldering to burst into flame. And even in these cases it is not something that is *applied*. The idea of a man who keeps a sex manual under the bed and refers to it several times nightly has often been the subject of jokes and cartoons, because it shows the absurd naivete of a person who treats bodies like car engines.

The true pleasure of sex lies in the spontaneous and passionate expression of erotic feelings. Theory learned from books or any other sources is useful in that it gives ideas of what might be expected or attempted, but once you are between the sheets, sensation, not theory, is your true guide.

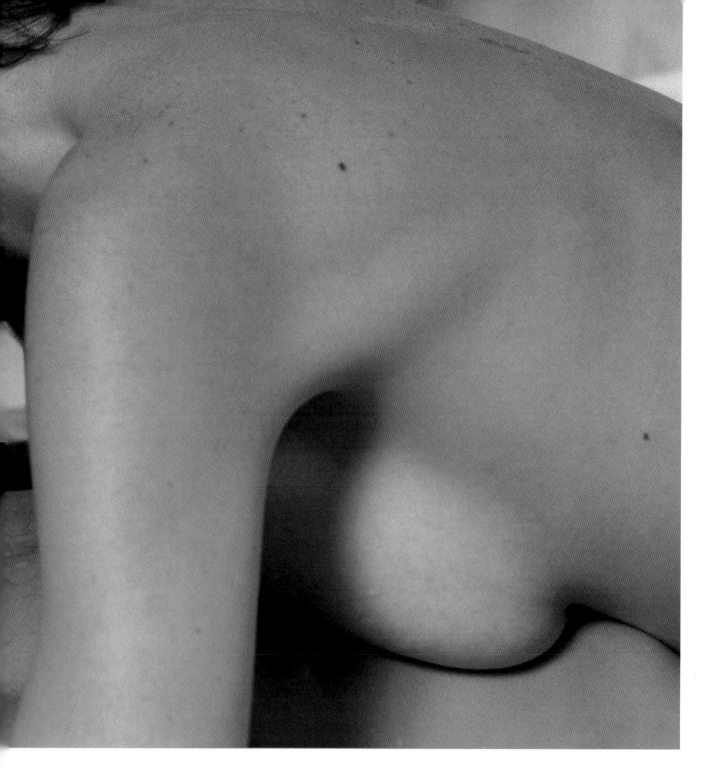

KISSING

There is an infinite variety of kisses that lovers can exchange, from playful or tender lip kissing to deeply arousing open-mouth kissing with tongue play. The lovers' kiss or French kiss, involving the whole mouth and tongue, is said to have its origins in the way mothers used to feed their babies in prehistoric cultures. This practice can be observed in peasant communities in some parts of Europe even today.

The mother chews the food for her baby before transferring it directly from mouth to mouth. She pushes her tongue, and the food, inside the infant's mouth, and it reacts with searching movements of its tongue inside her mouth. Considerations of hygiene and today's associations of mouth-to-mouth contact with sexual arousal make this type of feeding unacceptable in our society, but the action lives on in adult erotic behaviour.

A deep kiss is very often the first mutual acknowledgement that sexual attraction exists *between a couple, and it is the first element of sexuality to disappear from a relationship that is on the wane. According to Relate (the Marriage Guidance Bureau), couples whose marriages are in trouble are more likely to have intercourse than to kiss. That mouth and tongue contact retain a special intimacy while intercourse can seem businesslike and remote is also illustrated by the fact that prostitutes rarely kiss their clients.*

WHAT HAPPENS WHEN WE KISS

Deep sexual kissing with someone who really turns you on can be so exciting that you feel you might black out. Kissing makes the pulse race and shortens the breath. Only mouth-to-genital contact is a more powerful sexual stimulant than mouth-to-mouth kissing, which is why plenty of passionate kissing is, without doubt, the best possible kind of foreplay.

When we kiss, groups of sebaceous glands that developed inside the mouth at puberty are stimulated to release substances which are called semiochemicals. An exchange of semiochemicals between two people who are attracted to each other heightens sexual desire, and so the more they kiss, the more semiochemicals they release, which (partly) explains why lovers just can't stop kissing each other. Prolonged kissing makes the face flushed and the delicate skin around a woman's mouth swollen and red, mimicking the vaginal lips and inviting intercourse.

According to dentists, passionate kissing results in a surprising benefit for the teeth, because it activates the saliva glands and lowers the level of acidity in the mouth. This can help prevent tooth decay and the build-up of plaque.

THE ART OF KISSING

Kissing someone you are mad about is one of life's great pleasures – or should be. Surprisingly large numbers of people have no idea how to kiss, and a poor kisser can be a terrible disappointment, just as someone who is a skilled practitioner of the art of kissing can have you tearing off your clothes.

The first thing to do when kissing a new lover is to find out with your lips and tongue where his or her teeth are, so you can avoid banging into them with your own teeth. Clashing teeth is as impersonal as clashing spectacle frames. The next thing to remember is that kissing should be wildly exciting: don't get stuck in a rut endlessly repeating the same movement, or your partner will lose concentration and grow bored. Vary the pace, and vary the initiative, sometimes taking it yourself, sometimes being receptive to your partner.

Here are a few ideas:
● Drop lots of light kisses on your partner's parted lips until he or she begs you to use your tongue.
● Tickle the very corners of your partner's mouth with the tip of your tongue, occasionally pressing hard so that your tongue slides briefly inside his or her mouth. This can be almost unbearably arousing for the one who is kissed – and pretty exciting for the kisser too.
● With a firm tongue, lick your partner's whole mouth in long sensuous movements, as if you were enjoying an ice cream. Your partner should be lying down with head well back and lips parted, so that you can work luxuriously from one corner of the mouth to the other.
● Explore every part of your partner's mouth with your tongue.
● Thrust deeply with your tongue in and out of your partner's mouth, imitating the movement of the penis during intercourse. Men find this just as arousing as women do.

ALL-OVER BODY KISSING

Take time to kiss your partner all over. Proceed gently to avoid ticklish spots – waist, sides, soles of feet are common – as tickling causes squirming and flinching, which are definitely not erotic responses. Discover the places your partner likes best to be licked and kissed, and home in on those, circling them with tantalizing feather-light movements of the tongue, then increasing the pressure. Genitals are bound to be the favourites, so save them until last (see Oral sex, p. 90).

Most women – and some men – experience a special thrill from having their breasts kissed and licked, and their nipples sucked and flicked with a firm tongue until the tissue erects. Some women can even reach orgasm this way. Other particularly sensitive places might be in the crook of the arm, on the inside of the wrist, the inner thighs, the sides and back of the neck, the shoulders and all down the spine. Give your partner a massage with your tongue, starting with gentle kisses around the neck, then swooping round the shoulders and pressing down hard with your tongue as you rub up and down the vertebrae.

TIPS FOR MORE ENJOYABLE KISSING
● If your new partner does not smoke and you do, now would be a very good time to give up the habit. Non-smokers do not like the taste or smell of tobacco.
● At least until you have got to know someone well and they have assured you they don't mind it, don't eat strong tasting food, such as garlic or curry, unless your lover is eating it too.
● Oral hygiene is important. Make sure your mouth looks and tastes good. Get your dentist to descale your teeth regularly and eat a healthy diet so that your breath is fresh.
● Don't kiss or have oral sex if you have a

mouth or throat infection. Kissing can transfer an estimated 250 different bacteria and viruses carried in saliva, though as yet there is no evidence to suggest that AIDS can be caught in this way.

● Being kissed passionately by a man with a stubbly chin is not anywhere near as erotic as being kissed passionately by a man who has recently shaved.

● If you have a beard, consider the fact that it makes a barrier between your skin and your lover's. There is no doubt that more erotic contact is possible between a clean-shaven man and his partner.

● Women who wear make-up should be prepared to have it licked off or, at the very least, smudged. Consider how you feel about this before applying your make-up, but whatever you do, don't let yourself be inhibited by a perfectly painted face. Many men would prefer to kiss a face bare of make-up anyway.

● To maximize sensation when kissing, make full use of all the muscles in your mouth and tongue. It is much better kissing someone whose mouth responds to yours and who knows how to use pressure, than someone whose mouth is flabby and slack.

● Nothing is worse than a slobbery kiss.

MASTURBATION

The simple practice of giving oneself sexual pleasure has always caused an enormous amount of outrage, fear and confusion. The Old Testament railed against it, and the legacy of this reaction is still with us today in the form of jokes about going blind and growing hairs on the palms of the hands. Unfortunately, despite the fact that logic tells them otherwise, some people still believe that self-stimulation is harmful. Masturbation cannot cause mental or physical illness, debility or exhaustion. It is a natural and healthy method of sexual release engaged in by most people and many animal species. It is also an important part of learning one's own sexual response. Women who can bring themselves to orgasm by masturbating are more likely to have

orgasms with their partners, and men who can masturbate for 15 or 20 minutes without ejaculating are less likely to suffer from problems of premature ejaculation during intercourse.

FEMALE MASTURBATION

The fact that women could and did bring themselves to orgasm was not widely accepted until the sexual revolution of the 1960s. Before then, it was generally assumed that sexual pleasure was the domain of men, and that women who enjoyed their own bodies were whores. In Kinsey's survey, only 62 per cent of women said they masturbated. A quarter of a century later, Shere Hite found that 75 per cent of her female subjects did so. The jump in the figures could be due as much to the feeling that female masturbation had become more

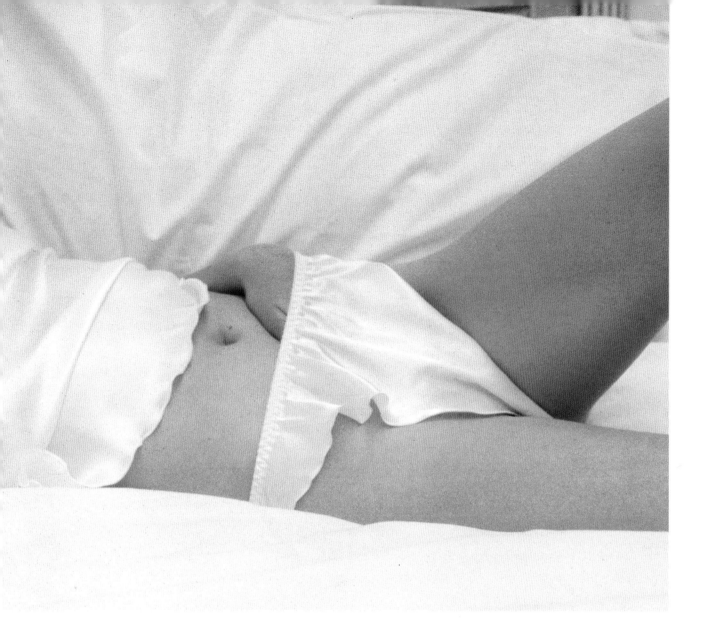

acceptable by the mid-1970s, as to the fact that more women had learned that it was available to them. In the '90s, it is to be hoped that the figures are higher still, especially among single women, but also among women with regular and permanent partners. Masturbation is a way of keeping in touch with yourself that should not be ignored. It can also sometimes be shared with a partner.

Kinsey found that women had more different techniques of bringing themselves to orgasm than men. He listed six different methods, which were used singly or in combination.

● By stimulation of the clitoris and the inner vaginal lips with one or two fingers. This was the first and most common method of achieving orgasm.

● By rubbing the outer vaginal lips and the whole of the genital area.

● By crossing the legs and repeatedly contracting and releasing the genital and thigh muscles.

● By lying face down or on the back and rhythmically contracting all the muscles of the body as in intercourse.

● By stimulating the nipples either by squeezing, pulling and rubbing them with the fingertips, or by brushing them very lightly with the palm of the hand.

● By vaginal penetration with the fingers or an object such as a vibrator.

This last method was practised by only 20 per cent of Kinsey's sample who masturbated. Many men assumed that women achieved satisfaction during masturbation only from penetration, and this proved them wrong, deluded by the importance they placed on their own genitals. Shere Hite's interviewees added a further method of reaching orgasm to the list: by stimulation with a jet of warm water from a shower head.

EXPLORING THE FEMALE GENITALS

Masturbation is an important part of getting to know your own body. If the sight of your own genitals is not familiar to you, examine them in a hand mirror while you relax after a bath or shower. The external genitals are called the vulva. Pubic hair grows on the labia majora, and inside these outer vaginal lips are the labia minora, which are pinker and moister. The clitoris is situated where they join at the top. It is a pink knob about the size of a dried pea, and is highly sensitive. The clitoris is protected by a hood, which retracts during sexual arousal (see p. 40). Below the clitoris is the tiny opening of the urethra, through which urine passes, and below that is the opening to the vagina.

When you start to masturbate, make sure you have plenty of time during which you won't be interrupted. Go somewhere where it is quiet, completely private, and warm. Some women like to lie on their back, some on their front; some like their legs pressed tightly together, others like them spread wide apart, or propped up above the body. Use a lubricant and stroke yourself gently, with your fingers or an object such as a vibrator, varying your movements from time to time to find out where and how you like to be stimulated.

Many women find the clitoris too sensitive for direct stimulation, so you could begin by rubbing the whole vulva, then gradually move inside with delicate fingers. Allow yourself to fantasize to increase arousal. Be patient, but if the pleasure wears off without your having had an orgasm, then you should stop. Don't be disappointed with yourself, as it may take several sessions before you can relax enough to really let go and enjoy it.

When you feel a gathering tension in the vaginal area and a build-up of warmth, orgasm is on the way. Continue to stimulate yourself, as if

you stop, these sensations will fade and it may be difficult to get them back again. The clitoris becomes increasingly sensitive as you proceed, whether you are stimulating it directly or not, and then orgasm breaks out with waves of vaginal contractions. Most women like some form of genital contact during orgasm: either continued stimulation or pressing or holding the vaginal area. Some like to insert a finger into the vagina as they come.

MALE MASTURBATION

Even though they were told that masturbation was 'self-abuse', more men than women were unable to resist the pleasure it gave them, according to Kinsey. Of his sample, 90 per cent of men admitted to masturbating, and they found only one harmful effect: it made many of them feel anxious and guilty. Kinsey and other sexologists after him have done much to dispel that anxiety and guilt, but such is the power of conditioning that some men still experience it today. Men who are furtive when they masturbate and bring themselves to orgasm as fast as possible to minimize guilt are likely to have problems with premature ejaculation during intercourse.

Boys usually discover masturbation earlier than girls. The penis is after all a difficult organ to ignore, especially when erect, and the natural inclination is to touch it. Shere Hite's male interviewees described various methods of giving themselves pleasure. Most men (82 per cent) stimulated the penis directly by hand. Of the remainder, most lay face down and rubbed themselves against the bed. A few pushed the erect penis down between their legs and rotated their hips. A few used water pressure, either from a shower head or in a jacuzzi. A very few (0.3 per cent) had managed to give themselves fellatio; and one had even achieved anal sex with himself!

EXPLORING THE MALE GENITALS

Most men are expert at giving themselves pleasure, but there's no harm in extra practice. A good way of finding out exactly how your genitals respond to stimulation is by soaping and gentle massage in the bath, allowing yourself to fantasize as you do so. Some men enjoy fondling their testicles, and some enjoy penetrating the anus with a finger. There are many different strokes you can use on the penis. If you are uncircumcized, you can draw the foreskin over the head of the penis and then pull it back down the shaft to get an erection; if you are circumcized, repeated squeezing round the shaft and letting go is usually effective. Then you can let your hand glide up and down the shaft in long slow movements, gradually building up speed and pressure. You may enjoy rubbing or tickling the glans of the penis, though for some men this is too sensitive. You may like gentle or firm pulling, stroking, squeezing and stretching. Try holding off ejaculation by varying the stroke when you become too excited, before finally letting go in orgasm.

MASTURBATION AND YOUR PARTNER

Masturbation need not be something that you do only when you are alone. Many people find the sight of their partner masturbating highly erotic. It can also be very instructive to discover how your partner reaches orgasm alone, as this will be the best method for you to adopt when you are masturbating him or her. Masturbating with your partner will break down inhibitions and allow you to get even closer.

Masturbating your partner in the way he or she enjoys is an important part of lovemaking, and many women like being masturbated to orgasm before penetration. Both men and women need to learn how to handle each other's genitals with tenderness and sensitivity. Read the sections above on exploring the genitals and experiment with your partner, proceeding gently and moderating or increasing your movements according to his or her response.

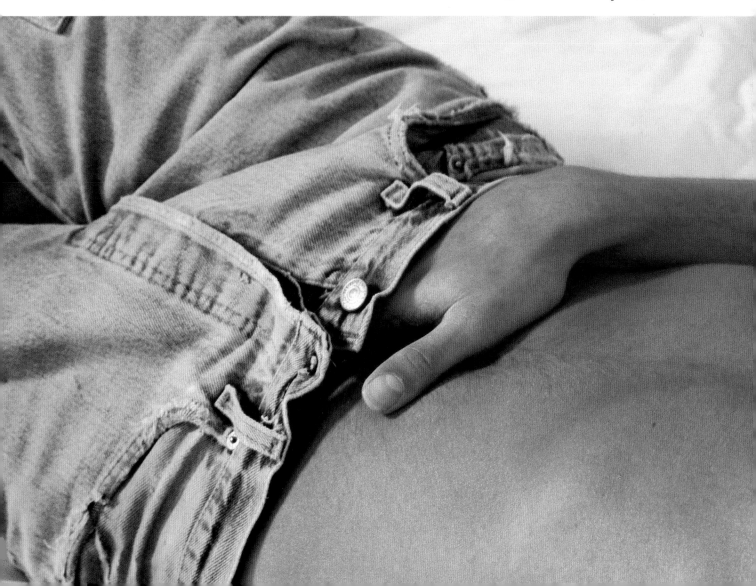

ORAL SEX

Oral sex begins with the first deep kiss, and continues with kisses all over the body, concentrating finally on the genitals. For many people, and particularly for women, oral sex offers the most sensual pleasure imaginable. To lie back and receive complete, luxurious and very detailed attention from the lips and tongue of someone you love is pure heaven.

On the part of the giver it requires a degree of emotional involvement, because it must be done with patience, tenderness, sensitivity and mounting but controlled excitement if it is to be really good. Lovers who give oral sex reluctantly and without generosity or enjoyment make their partners feel guilty and selfish, and too tense and worried to relax and take pleasure themselves.

From the receiver, oral sex requires trust, and the confidence that comes with being made to feel desirable. In sex, as in other areas of life, it is often more difficult to receive generosity than to give it, but the person who succumbs completely to pleasure delivers himself or herself over to the lover, and this also gives a sense of wonderment.

It goes without saying that sexual hygiene is of prime importance for anyone who engages in oral sex (see p. 134).

CUNNILINGUS

For many women, oral sex is the most exciting of all the variations of sex, and a gentle and skilful lover should be able to make his partner come with his tongue more easily than in any other way. A strong slippery tongue can be used with precision on the clitoris without danger of causing any pain, unlike a finger.

Shere Hite reported that 42 per cent of her female interviewees orgasmed through cunnilingus. The reason more women do not come in this way is likely to be that their partners do not give them long enough. In addition, some women feel that enjoying themselves like this is selfish, because their partners might get bored, or be repulsed by the taste or smell of their genitals. A lover who really cares about his partner's pleasure will get a special thrill out of arousing her and bringing her to orgasm with his tongue, and his own enjoyment should reassure her that there is nothing unpleasant about it.

Begin by kissing your partner's face and mouth, and then gradually work your way down her body, kissing and stroking her breasts, belly and inner thighs. Flick your tongue in light feathery kisses along the fleshy folds of the outer labia, smoothing away the pubic hair and then parting the labia gently with your fingers. Try not to get too many pubic hairs in your mouth, as it will spoil your partner's enjoyment if you stop while you laboriously pull them out. Move very gradually inwards with your tongue. Vary your movements according to your partner's response. Try nuzzling, burrowing, thrusting with your tongue into her vagina, sucking, long delicate licks, short rapid flicking licks. She may not like her clitoris to be stimulated directly at first, so proceed tentatively until she is fully aroused. Some women like a man to use his fingers as well as his tongue, while others find too many sensations distracting.

Once she can trust you and feel confident that you like what you are doing, she will be able fully to let go in orgasm. Being 'on the spot', you will be able to see and feel all the stages of arousal to climax much better than when you are inside her, or masturbating her and kissing her mouth at the same time. A man can get a special thrill from experiencing so directly the blissful effect he has on his partner, as well as from her vulnerability and trust.

FELLATIO

The experience of having their penis sucked, licked and kissed is one that most men find intensely exciting. In some cases, there may be psychological barriers to overcome. A man may feel that he does not want to 'subject' his lover to licking his genitals. A sensitive and sensual woman who genuinely cares for her partner will, however, get a great deal of pleasure herself out of arousing him in this way. Some men fear being bitten during oral sex. The woman should

open her mouth as wide as possible, and close her lips, but not her teeth, over the penis. Using all the muscles in the lips and tongue will mean that the teeth should not come into contact with the penis at all.

Some women are worried that they may be choked during fellatio. The way to allay this fear is to remain in control: you are the one who should move while your partner lies still, so there is no possibility of his thrusting deep into your throat and making you gag. You can also grip the base of the penis with your fingers to limit penetration.

Some women find the idea of swallowing semen repugnant. Of course there is no need for you to do this if you do not wish to, and you can always bring your partner to orgasm through masturbation or inside your vagina, but many women do enjoy having their partner ejaculate into their mouth. It is worth noting that semen swallowed immediately does not have the set, jelly-like consistency of semen drying on a bed sheet, and can be as delightful as hot milk with honey. Each man's semen, like each woman's vaginal juices, tastes slightly different, and, like the taste of your lover's sweat or his saliva, it is a part of his individual body chemistry that you may find highly arousing.

Begin by kissing your partner's face and mouth, and then work your way down his body to his genitals. Some men like to have their testicles sucked and licked; others do not. Be very gentle, as they are highly sensitive to pain. There are many ways of stimulating the penis with your lips and tongue. You can lick all along the shaft with a delicate tongue, then use more pressure and press your open lips as well as your tongue against it as you rub them up and down towards the head. You can lick and kiss the frenulum – the sensitive place where the glans joins the shaft on the underside, which will be facing towards you if the man is lying on his back with an erection. You can take the head of the penis in your mouth and suck it, tickling it at the same time with your tongue, and you can move your lips as far down the shaft as is comfortable, and then move up and down,

sucking and pressing with your lips and tongue.

The more saliva you use, the easier it will be. Use your fingers too, to stimulate the shaft of the penis while you are sucking the head. Slide a finger up inside your mouth and tickle the glans with your finger as well as with your tongue. The more inventive you get, the more you will enjoy it, and the more pleasure you will give. Don't feel pressured to keep up an 'in-and-out' movement to simulate intercourse, as you will soon tire of this and your mouth will begin to ache. Take your time, vary your movements, and if you both want your partner to come inside your mouth, suck hard as he is about to ejaculate and swallow several times until there is no semen left. You will probably feel as good as the Russian Empress Catherine the Great, who reputedly took a draught of semen every morning before breakfast.

'SIXTY-NINE'
The 'sixty-nine' position (*soixante-neuf*, in French) is so called after the shape two bodies make when they engage in mutual oral-genital stimulation. While this can be very exciting, many couples find it distracting to concentrate on more than one sensation at a time, and 69 is extremely demanding. It is difficult to give your lover your full attention and remain entirely receptive to what he or she is doing for you, at the same time avoiding strain on arms, legs and other parts of the body that might get in the way. It may be interesting to try, but perhaps not ultimately satisfying. You may like to just look at or gently touch your partner's genitals while receiving oral sex.

RIMMING
This is the name given to oral-anal contact. The anus is highly sensitive and many men and women enjoy anal kissing and licking as part of oral sex, or as a prelude to anal sex (see p. 71 and p. 93). Another way of stimulating the anus is with the fingers. Obviously hygiene is of the utmost importance, both for your partner's enjoyment and also because of the danger of transmitting disease (p. 134).

INTERCOURSE

Intercourse usually comes last on the love-making menu because it is during intercourse that a man is most likely to let go and climax. After ejaculation, he may naturally feel more like resting for a while than continuing to stimulate his partner, and so it may be preferable for her to come before intercourse.

Most women do not have orgasms during intercourse, though an amazing one-third of all Shere Hite's female interviewees said that they faked them to spare their own or their partner's ego. Faking puts a barrier of misunderstanding between you and your partner at the deepest possible level. How then can you expect to trust each other at any other level?

It is not necessary to have an orgasm during intercourse for a woman to find it both exciting and extremely satisfying. Intercourse allows for all-over, inside-and-outside closeness, and for a pair of lovers who are highly sensitized towards one another, it provides the most intimate form of communication of erotic love. Intercourse with someone you love passionately is an amazing experience because it can get better as your emotions for your lover develop. Though you may go through the same motions, there are endless thrilling sensations that make each time entirely different and take you closer towards knowing each other, and knowing yourself.

WHICH POSITION?
There are many positions in which penetration can take place – one enterprising author has managed to count 3,780 of them – but a great number of these are variations dependent on the position of an individual limb. Anyone who is enthusiastic about their partner will naturally want to try out different positions, and continue to practise those that suit the best. Your favourite positions will be those in which you can most comfortably relax, as undue strain on any part of the body is at best distracting and at worst dangerous. One of the most comfortable will undoubtedly be the missionary position. Other positions you may choose for their sheer erotic impact, for deep penetration, or for a view of your partner that you find particularly arousing: perhaps a split-level position, or entry from behind. See Sex positions p. 98.

Spontaneous choice is more exciting than pre-planning, though you may get a lot of fun out of talking about what you intend to do next, and variety is important. Of course, if you are both sleepy, you may just naturally fall into the missionary position, but if you are spending the day in bed, adventurous ideas are called for.

To make yourselves comfortable, ensure complete privacy and a warm room. Being under the blankets all the time is inhibiting, and so is cold air. Ideally, there should also be a warm bathroom not too far away. If it is dark, candles or a soft night-light will be much kinder on the eyes than bright overhead illumination. Have lots of pillows on the bed: you may want to use them under the buttocks or lower back.

ANAL SEX
Surveys indicate that anal sex is not often proposed by women, and that they are likely to fear it is unhygienic and painful. Of course, it can be both. You should be scrupulous about cleanliness, and a man should take special care to be gentle when entering his partner anally. You are more likely to contract AIDS (see p. 136) through anal penetration than through any other sexual activity, because the membrane lining the rectum is so thin that a virus can easily enter through it. If there is a danger that your partner might be HIV-positive, he should wear a condom.

If precautions are observed and both parties are enthusiastic, anal sex can offer a different type of intimacy. The rectum is usually tighter than the vagina, but, as the woman relaxes, she can allow really deep penetration, especially if she is on all-fours with her partner kneeling behind her. He should not thrust too hard, especially until he is right inside, and should be guided by her hip movements.

Always make sure that you wash anything – penis, fingers, vibrator – after it has been inside the anus, and never transfer anything from the anus to the vagina without washing.

MASSAGE

Massage is probably the oldest form of therapy in the world. It can be used to relieve pain, to soothe, to relax and to stimulate. Between lovers, massage can also communicate tender, caring and erotic feelings. If your lover is tired and tense, or suffering from aching limbs, massage can induce a deep feeling of wellbeing and end in a rejuvenating sleep. If he or she is wide awake, but too tense and distracted to make love, massage can relax the body and clear the mind, making way for erotic response.

It is as much pleasure to give an erotic massage as to receive one. The room where you are should be warm, draught-free, completely private and softly lit. It is often more comfortable for the massager to be able to stand up to work, and you can make an ideal 'couch' from a large table topped with blankets and a sheet. If your table is not long enough to accomodate your lover's body at full stretch, then use your bed, or spread a blanket out on the floor in front of the fire.

PREPARING FOR MASSAGE

- Make your lover comfortable with pillows.
- Both of you should remove all jewellery.
- Ensure your nails are short, and not sharp.
- Do not talk during the massage, except to check that what you are doing is pleasurable.
- Before you begin the massage, relax your hands and wrists by shaking them.
- Make sure you are sitting, kneeling or standing in a comfortable and balanced position, as any awkwardness or tension will transmit itself directly to your partner. Keep your back straight and move from your pelvis.
- A massage oil or cream will enable your hands to move smoothly over your lover's body. The most luxurious oils are those used for aromatherapy, which contain plant essences, but you could also use almond oil or baby oil.
- Keep the oil close to you, but put it where you will not knock it over.
- Warm the oil before use by rubbing it between your palms; never drip it directly on to your lover's body.

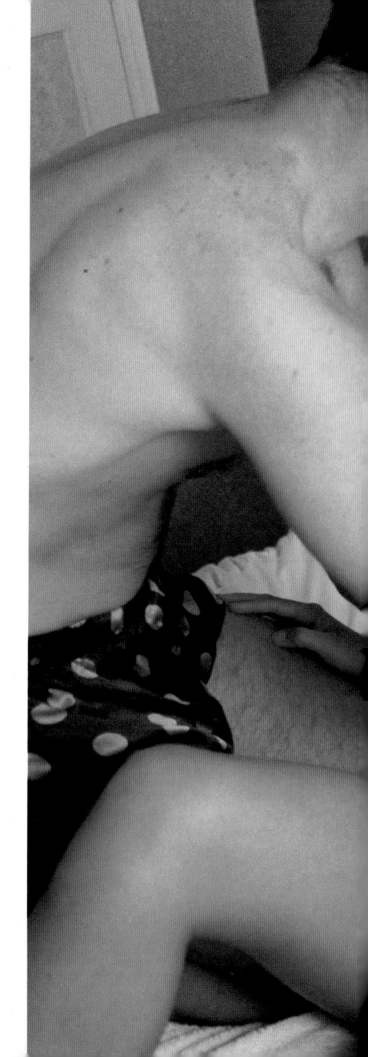

MASSAGE STROKES

Massage strokes should always begin with the lightest touch, gradually increasing in concentration and pressure until you reach below the soft flesh and the superficial muscles to massage the joints. Once areas of tension have been thoroughly smoothed out, you can start to relax the pressure and end as lightly as you began.

For an erotic massage, you might decide to give your lover a complete back massage with deep pressure, then work lightly and gently from the neck down the chest to the belly and upper thighs, circling in to the genitals. When you get to the genitals, your partner may become very enthusiastic and want to join in. However, you should insist that the massage is not over. Your partner should remain passive while you continue with rhythmic stimulation, following the movements you know your partner enjoys during masturbation, until you bring him or her to orgasm.

● Use light strokes to begin and end the massage and to move from one part of the body to another. These strokes should be broad, fluent and soothing, reminiscent of water flowing smoothly over the flesh. Mould your palms and fingers into the contours of your lover's body as your hands glide effortlessly across it.

● Begin to work more deeply and more specifically, pulling and kneading rhythmically, one hand echoing the movement of the other. Stretch the flesh under your hands, then let it relax. Don't grab, but keep your hands on the body, rocking back on the heel of your hand between movements.

● Once your partner is completely relaxed you can progress to really penetrating strokes, working concentratedly with the ball of the thumb, fingertips and the heel of the hand. Push rhythmically, describing tiny circles. Use your body weight. Be as firm as you can without hurting your partner.

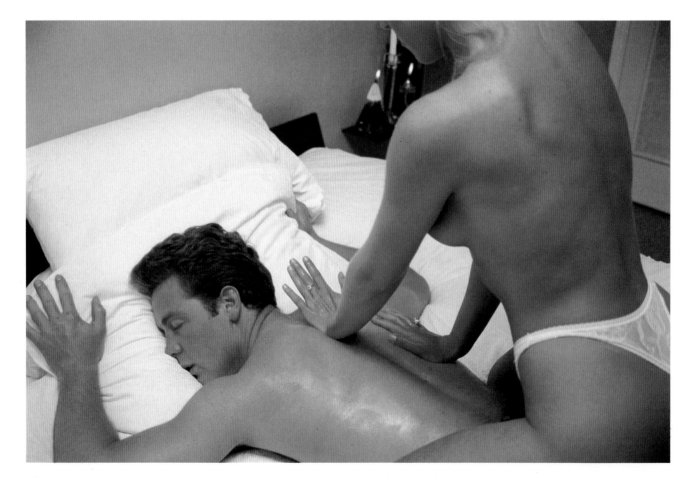

LE CHAPEAU, 1984

SEX POSITIONS

The missionary is the most commonly adopted lovemaking position, because it is so comfortable, but there are many different ways of enjoying each other's bodies, and each of the positions illustrated here may suggest another into which you can move.

Some positions offer greater intimacy, with all-over body contact and the opportunity to embrace and kiss; others offer deeper penetration; some are quite difficult to maintain, which creates its own urgency and excitement. Adventurous lovers will find variations of their own, either by design or by chance: you may get overtaken by lust half way up the stairs or while talking in the kitchen.

The important thing is to engage all your instincts and follow your feelings, while remaining acutely aware of your partner's responses.

SIDE BY SIDE

. . . .

This position, with the lovers lying side by side and facing one another, is easy to slip into after mutual masturbation, and can be a prelude to rolling over with either partner on top. Here, the woman has her leg wrapped round her partner's body to facilitate deeper penetration: she pulls him towards her with her leg as he thrusts. The partners can kiss and touch each other's genitals while making love in this position.

SPLIT LEVEL

....

This is one of a number of 'split-level' positions that gives the partners a different view of each other and a different angle of penetration.

Here, the woman lies on her back, her legs round her partner's waist, while he kneels. He is in total control, and can also stimulate her clitoris with his fingers.

From this position he can let her legs drop and lie on top of her in the missionary position, or he can raise her legs, resting them around his shoulders, then bend forward to kiss her mouth, at the same time gaining depth of penetration.

FIRESIDE

In this cosy position, which can follow
cunnilingus, the woman sits comfortably in
an armchair with her arms and legs around
the man, who enters kneeling in front of her.
If she leans back, he can support himself with
his hands on the back of the chair, which will
allow him more thrust.

COUCH

. . . .

For this position you need to try out all your furniture to find a piece of the correct height. The woman lies on the edge of a table, couch or bed covered with quilts and pillows, and spreads her legs wide. The man can begin by kneeling to give her cunnilingus, then, as here, he stands to enter her, supporting himself on one knee and holding her ankles.

This affords him a great deal of control, and the angle of penetration is steep.

SWIMMING

The man lies on his back, spreading his legs, and his partner lies on top of him, her legs along his, her feet on his. There is a good opportunity for kissing and total body contact. She controls the pace of lovemaking by dragging herself up and down against him. Many women find this position very exciting, and are more likely to reach orgasm without direct clitoral stimulation this way than any other.

She can vary the position by closing her legs tightly while his remain spread, or by getting him to close his, or both. She can also move easily from this position to sit up facing him.

SPOONS

The 'spoons' position is so named because of the close fit of the two bodies. The partners lie on their sides and the man enters from behind. This position is cosy and relaxing, good for slow drowsy lovemaking prior to falling asleep, or on waking during the night.

It is also a comfortable position to adopt later in pregnancy when most others put too much pressure on the woman's belly.

LAP

. . . .

This is a position that may suggest itself while cuddling on the sofa. The man sits with the woman straddling his lap, facing him. She controls the pace, they can kiss and he can caress her breasts. She moves up and down on him, supporting herself with her knees on the sofa, and her arms round his neck.

If they use a dining chair, she can keep her feet on the floor and hold on to the chair back for support if necessary. If she faces away from him, they will be able to achieve deeper penetration, and she could support herself against furniture in front of her.

SPREADEAGLE

In this rear entry position, the woman lies
face down with the man on top of her. She
spreads her legs and he supports his weight on
his arms. If she raises her bottom off the bed
slightly, perhaps with the aid of a pillow
under her hips, then it will be possible to
achieve deeper penetration.

The man can also lie with his full weight
on his partner, from which position it is easy
to roll into 'spoons' (p. 105).

CUISSADE

....

This position is known as 'cuissade', from the French cuisse, thigh. The woman lies on her back, with the man at her side. She raises the leg nearest to him and rests it on his body, and he enters from under her thigh, with his nearest leg crossing her body.

They can hold one another and kiss, and the position is a very intimate one, possible because of the 'secretive' form of entry. The woman can exert a certain amount of restraint with her thigh, which can make it more exciting.

CRAWL

··

Deep penetration can be achieved with the woman on all fours and her partner kneeling behind her. This position gives both lovers the opportunity to thrust hard against one another, and the man may also caress his partner's breasts, buttocks and clitoris.

Rear entry positions like this one are ideal when both partners are in the mood for vigorous rather than tender lovemaking.

A variation is for both partners to stand with the woman bending forward and supporting herself against furniture.

CROSS
....

Here the woman lies on her back on the bed and the man lies diagonally across her. She opens her legs to allow him to enter and he rocks gently from side to side. She can guide his movements with the pressure of her hands. This position is somewhat easier to maintain if the man lies beneath on his back and the woman is in control.

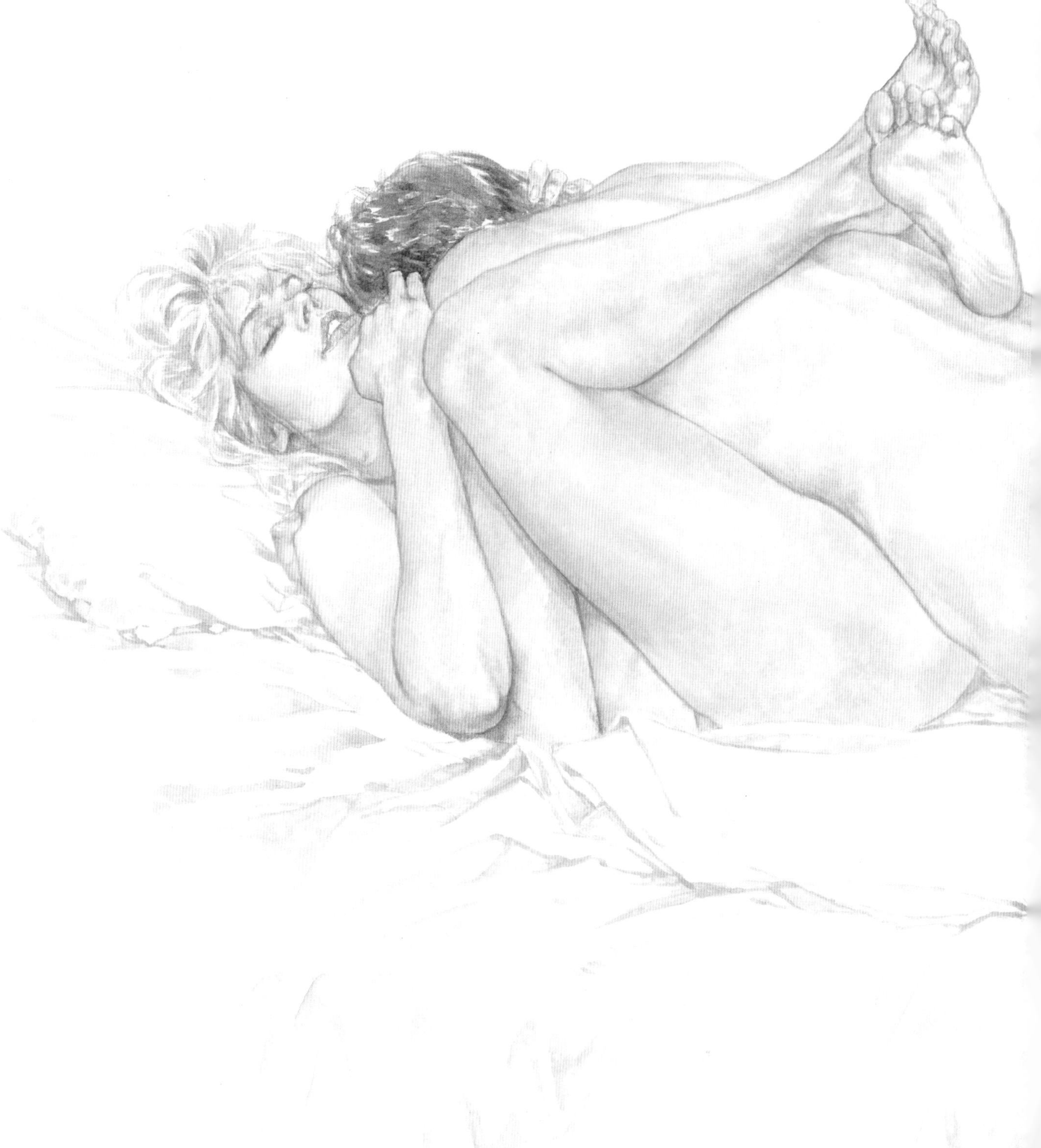

MISSIONARY

The missionary position is the most popular lovemaking position of all because it is comfortable, affords a great deal of body contact and good depth of penetration. The lovers can kiss and hold each other at the same time. The woman lies on her back with her legs spread and her knees raised, and her partner lies on top between her legs.

From this position the woman can move to clasp her legs behind her partner's back or to close them tightly underneath him, while he spreads his.

STANDING CARRY

The man stands, holding his partner in his arms. She wraps her legs round his waist and her arms round his shoulders. She can move against him by pulling herself up and down, and he can help her with his arms. This position can be assumed from sitting. It can, of course, be adopted in a very confined space, but is quite strenuous.

From this position you can return to sitting, or the man can gently lower his partner on to a bed or preferably a table, where thrusting can continue without so much exertion.

HEAD TO TOE

The man lies on his back with his legs spread and his penis inside the woman, who also lies down on her back, with her legs spread across his, her toes pointing to his head, and her head away from him. The woman is in control. The partners cannot see each other, or touch each other anywhere except on the feet and ankles. Thus sensation is concentrated solely on the genitals.

This position can be adopted from one in which the lovers sit on the bed facing one another, their legs interlaced.

FELLATIO

In fellatio, the woman sucks, licks, kisses and strokes her partner's penis. Exquisitely satisfying for the man, fellatio can also give enormous erotic pleasure to the woman as she senses his responses and his total abandonment to her.

For more about fellatio, see p. 90.

CUNNILINGUS

In cunnilingus, the man stimulates his partner's vulva and clitoris with his lips and tongue. For most women, cunnilingus gives the most delicious sensual pleasure and is the best way of climaxing. It is also extremely arousing for the partner.

For more about cunnilingus, see p. 90.

LEGS OVER

The woman lies on her back with her legs raised and wrapped around the man's shoulders. He supports himself on his arms above her.

This position affords deep penetration, and can be helped by placing a pillow under her buttocks. He can lean forward to kiss her, and because her legs seem to be pushing him away, though both her mouth and her vagina invite him, this is a position that can be very exciting.

If the woman's legs or the man's arms get too tired, the couple can relax into the missionary position.

STANDING

Both parties stand, using the wall as support. This position is often used when the desire to make love strikes unexpectedly. Part of the excitement lies in the fact that it is not easy to move in this position.

URGENT
. . . .

This position is ideal for when you are unexpectedly overtaken by the urge to make love. It does not even require more than a loosening of the clothes if you want. The woman leans over the nearest available piece of furniture and the man enters from behind.

This is ideal for fast exciting sex and gives both partners the opportunity to thrust against one another.

ASTRIDE

With the man lying on his back on the bed,
the woman can sit astride him and control
the pace of their lovemaking. Facing him, she
may squat on her haunches for a more
powerful bouncing movement, or, as here,
kneel, supporting herself with her hands.
This way, she is free to lean forward and kiss
his mouth.

From this position it is easy for her to
increase the intimacy by lying with her whole
body along his.

A variation is for her to face away from
him, increasing depth of penetration.

Sex Questions & Answers

The sexual relationship can be the greatest source of human pleasure, but it is also more fraught with anxiety than most other human bonds. This section of the book looks at some commonly experienced problems, both medical and emotional.

SEX AND HEALTH

There is no doubt that a fulfilling sexual relationship can boost good health, but sex and health are also connected in other ways that require serious consideration. The two major areas of concern are contraception and protection against sexually transmitted diseases, especially AIDS.

A survey carried out among young people in August 1991 showed that the majority of sexually active young women had taken responsibility for contraception by being on the Pill, but that though they were aware of the danger of AIDS, young people often had sex with a new partner without a condom, particularly if they had been drinking.

This revelation is extremely worrying. It is a mistake to think that the risk of AIDS is restricted to the homosexual population, to intravenous drug users and to haemophiliacs. These are certainly the highest-risk groups, but in America the fastest growing group of people infected with HIV is heterosexual women.

The insidious nature of the disease means that with unprotected sex, you are at risk not only from your present partner, but from each of his or her previous partners over the past four years, and that if you become infected you can infect your next four years' worth of partners, and any children they might bear, without even knowing it.

The message is clear: everyone should always use a condom until a relationship has become well established.

CONTRACEPTION

What is Natural Family Planning?

This is a natural method of contraception in which the woman works out when she is likely to conceive, and avoids intercourse on those days. A woman is fertile around the time of ovulation. An egg is released (ovulation) once a month, about 12-16 days before the start of her next period. The egg is capable of being fertilized for two days after ovulation, but as sperm may live for up to five days inside a woman intercourse should be avoided for that time prior to ovulation as well. Conception is most likely to be avoided if intercourse takes place only in the time after ovulation up to the next period.

There are a number of ways of learning to recognize the fertile time, including keeping body temperature charts and noting changes in the texture of cervical mucus. All these methods require some instruction so it is advisable to contact your doctor or clinic first.

The main disadvantage of NFP is that intercourse has to be avoided for a part of each month. It also necessitates keeping records and charts which some women find complicated or inconvenient.

How effective is NFP?

The most effective methods of Natural Family Planning is known as the Sympto-thermal Method and uses a combination of charting body temperature and cervical mucus with other signs to determine the time of ovulation. If used carefully, and with proper instruction it is 80-98% effective.

Is it possible to get pregnant if the man withdraws before orgasm?

Yes. The withdrawal method (coitus interruptus) is believed to be practised by as many as one in seven married couples, but it may not be satisfactory, either medically or psychologically. There may be some seminal fluid containing sperm on the tip of the man's penis before he ejaculates, and this could cause the woman to conceive. Also, semen on the woman's belly or thighs, or on a sheet, could get transferred to her vagina by the fingers, with the same result.

The idea is that the man withdraws his penis from the woman's vagina at the last minute and comes outside her body. This is quite difficult to do when excitement is mounting to the point of loss of control.

What is coitus reservatus?

This is sexual intercourse during which the man does not ejaculate. After penetration, the man lies still with his penis inside the woman and moves only slightly from time to time to keep his erection, never reaching the uncontrollable excitement that comes just before orgasm.

Coitus reservatus is not very popular because most couples would find it too frustrating. As a method of contraception, it is not satisfactory because it is very difficult not to lose control, and of course it carries the same risks as coitus interruptus, in that some seminal fluid may seep from the penis even without ejaculation.

In some Oriental cultures, coitus reservatus is practised regularly, and some men can train themselves to orgasm without ejaculating, which means developing muscle control to such a sensitive pitch that instead of being shot out of the penis, the semen is shot into the bladder and leaves the body in the urine.

What are the advantages of using the condom?

First of all, the condom is about 85-98 per cent effective as a method of contraception. Condoms are easy and cheap to buy, and simple to use. Like other 'barrier' methods of contraception, they work by preventing the sperm from getting to its destination, and they do not interfere with the body's chemistry. In recent years, when there have been some doubts about the side effects of the Pill, condoms have become popular.

Another important advantage of using a condom is that it protects against sexually transmitted diseases, such as HIV, the virus that causes AIDS. For this reason, anyone who engages in casual sex or is having sex with a new partner should use a condom even if contraceptive protection is provided by the Pill, and women as well as men are recommended to carry them.

What are the disadvantages of using the condom?

The main disadvantage of the condom is that it is a barrier method that is likely to create unwanted barriers between the lovers. Although condoms are made of the finest latex, the super-sensitivity of skin to skin is bound to be lost. The business of putting on the condom can also intrude on the mood of lovemaking. It may not be possible to relax completely when you know that you will have to interrupt what you are doing before you can go further. Both men and women sometimes suffer a loss of arousal when the condom is put on, though if the woman puts it on, it may feel less abrupt and businesslike.

Once the condom is on, there is the feeling that intercourse comes next and the condom will not be taken off until the man has ejaculated. This can make sex feel rather regimented, as, without a condom, the couple might prefer not to follow a set lovemaking 'menu'. To make using a condom more attractive manufacturers now produce them in different colours and

How to use a condom

Condoms come ready-rolled, and most end in a teat, which catches the semen.

● **Place the opening of the condom on the head of the penis and unroll it down the shaft until you reach the base.**

● **After ejaculation, the condom should be removed carefully to prevent spillage. First, the man withdraws his penis from the woman's vagina, holding the condom securely to his penis so as not to leave it behind. Then he removes it and disposes of it. Of course, care must always be taken that any semen left on the penis does not get transferred – on the fingers, for example – to the woman's vagina.**

● **Care should be taken to keep condoms away from heat, which may weaken the rubber, and not to snag them with the fingernails.**

with textural variations, such as small protrusions designed to stimulate the vagina. You can even buy strawberry or mint flavoured condoms.

Although condoms give a high guarantee of safety against conception and disease, many people do not like to use them on a long-term basis because they find them too intrusive, unaesthetic and impersonal.

What are caps and diaphragms?

These act as a contraceptive by forming a barrier across the neck of the womb (cervix), which prevents the sperm from reaching and fertilizing the egg. As a good fit is crucial, you need to be examined by your doctor or family planning clinic so that the right-sized cap or diaphragm can be chosen, and you can be shown how to insert it.

The most common type is the vaginal diaphragm: a dome of fine rubber on a flexible rim. It fits above and behind the pubic bone, the rim springing out to hug the walls of the vagina and the dome covering the cervix.

The cervical cap is smaller and rimless. It fits directly over the cervix, held in place by suction. There are three types of cap: the vault cap looks like a rimless diaphragm; the cervical cap, which looks like a rubber thimble; and the vimule cap, which looks like a hat with a deep brim.

What is the correct way to use a diaphragm or cap?

A cap or diaphragm should always be used with a spermicide. This combination has been found to be a 95 per cent safe contraceptive.

Smear a little spermicide on to the diaphragm and around the rim, to facilitate insertion. Squeeze the diaphragm into a boat shape and insert

it as you would a sanitary tampon, opening the lips of the vagina with one hand. When the rim rests behind the pubic bone at the front and the dome covers the cervix at the back, it is in place.

Spermicide is put inside the cap but not around the edge as this may prevent suction.

Doctors recommend that you should not leave the diaphragm or cap in place for longer than 24 hours, but you should wait for at least six hours after intercourse before removing it. Remember that spermicide will be effective only for about three hours, so you will need to put more into the vagina if you have intercourse after the diaphragm or cap has been in place for that length of time.

When you remove the diaphragm or cap, wash it carefully in warm soapy water and allow it to dry in a warm place, or pat gently with a towel.

Do I need regular check-ups if I use a diaphragm or cap?

After your diaphragm or cap has been fitted, you will be asked to return to the clinic a week later with it in place to check that the fit is good and that you are inserting it correctly. Usually, six-monthly check-ups are advisable thereafter. If you put on or take off more than half a stone (3kg), you may need a different size, and changes may also take place if you have an abortion, a miscarriage, or a baby.

Is it safe to use a spermicide without any other form of protection?

No. A spermicide is essentially a back-up device for use with barrier methods. Some couples also use a spermicide with a condom, although many condoms are now lubricated with a thin film of spermicidal cream.

What is an IUD?

The IUD (intrauterine device) is a small plastic and copper device that is inserted into the womb to prevent conception. This can be done only by a doctor trained in family planning. The IUD comes compressed in a thin tube, which is slid through the cervical canal into the uterus and then withdrawn, leaving the IUD to spring into shape.

There are thin threads hanging from the IUD about 1 inch (3cm) into the vagina, and these can be felt with the fingers to make sure that the device is still in place. When the IUD is removed, the doctor will do so by pulling the strings with a specially designed instrument.

Depending on type, IUDs are usually replaced about every five years.

The IUD is reckoned to be 96-99 per cent effective as a contraceptive.

How does the IUD work?

The IUD is thought to work in a number of ways. Research shows its main action is to stop the sperm reaching the egg to fertilize it. It may also delay the egg coming down the fallopian tube or prevent the egg from settling in the uterus.

What are the advantages of the IUD?

Once the IUD is in place, it is immediately effective as a contraceptive. It is even effective against pregnancy if it is inserted up to three days after intercourse has occurred. Many women like it because it frees both partners to be completely spontaneous in their lovemaking – there is no breaking off to put on a condom or insert a cap and not even a daily Pill to remember. Check-ups are necessary only once a year.

What are the disadvantages of the IUD?

For those women who are comfortable with the IUD, it can be a near-perfect form of contraception.

Some women experience discomfort and bleeding for a few hours or days after the IUD is inserted, and one in four women has to have it removed because of acute discomfort and heavy bleeding. Sometimes an IUD may fall out; this is more likely to happen during a period than at any other time, and this is why it is important to check regularly to feel the thin strings are still inside the vagina.

Finally, although the IUD is an effective protection against ordinary pregnancy, it does not protect against ectopic pregnancy, a rare phenomenon which occurs when a fertilized egg starts to develop in the fallopian tube.

Is there a danger of contraceptives or tampons getting stuck permanently inside the vagina?

As long as female barrier methods and tampons are correctly inserted with the fingers there should be no problem in removing them with the fingers. If you cannot do this yourself, your doctor will be able to do it.

If you are using a cap or diaphragm, the nurse instructing you on its use will show you how to remove it. It should be left in place for six hours after intercourse. If you forget to remove your diaphragm or a tampon, it may cause an infection after several days. Once you have removed it, the infection should clear up without medication, but if it does not, then you should consult your doctor. Never try to remove an IUD yourself (see above). This has to be done by a doctor or other trained person. If the

cords on the IUD are irritating your partner's penis, as occasionally happens, your doctor will be able to shorten them for you. Never put objects inside the vagina that were not designed to be put there.

How does the Pill work?

The combined Pill contains synthetic forms of the sex hormones oestrogen and progesteron, which interfere with the woman's regular 28-day menstrual cycle. In a woman who is not taking the Pill, production of the sex hormones fluctuates during the cycle, and it is this fluctuation that triggers ovulation. When the hormone level is kept artificially constant by the Pill, the signal to ovulate is cancelled out. The same happens during pregnancy, which is why overlapping pregnancies do not occur. The Pill is 93-97 per cent effective as a method of contraception.

The 'progestogen-only Pill', which is taken mainly by women over 35, is not, as is sometimes assumed, a low-dose Pill, but one containing a single hormone, progestogen. It has the effect of thickening the secretions in the cervix, which makes it difficult for the sperms to pass. It can be taken by breastfeeding mothers, unlike the combined Pill, which suppresses lactation. It is a slightly less reliable method of contraception than the Pill.

A Pill that can be taken vaginally was launched in the mid-1980s, and the advantage of this is that it eliminates the nausea some women feel on taking the Pill orally, although more research needs to be done to ensure that the coating on the Pill dissolves quickly and that the hormones are not absorbed by the man during intercourse. This method of contraception is not yet generally available.

What are the advantages of the Pill?

There are many advantages in using the Pill. The first is that it is up to 99 per cent reliable when taken according to instructions. The second, and, in many women's minds, an equally important point in its favour, is that it allows for completely spontaneous lovemaking. The freedom it gives must be of enormous psychological benefit in any relationship. The Pill also regulates the menstrual cycle and reduces period pain and heavy bleeding in many women. It can be prescribed solely for this purpose, and not as a contraceptive, to girls who are just beginning to menstruate.

What are the side-effects of taking the Pill?

In many cases there are no negative side-effects at all. However, some women experience mild side-effects that disappear after a few months. These may include nausea, headaches, depression, loss of sex drive, some bleeding between periods, vaginal discharge, swollen and sore breasts, and weight gain. If the side-effects persist, the doctor or clinic will usually recommend a change to a Pill with a lower oestrogen or progestogen content, or different progestogen content or a different method of contraception.

Before your doctor prescribes the Pill, he will ask you about the incidence of thrombosis and heart disease in your family. Anyone who smokes heavily is at risk from thrombosis, and smokers over 35 are advised not to take the combined Pill. You will also be asked about migraine, epilepsy and diabetes, and the doctor will want to check your blood pressure.

From time to time there are scares in the newspapers linking the Pill to various forms of cancer. Although no hard and fast conclusions have been reached (the Pill was only invented in 1956), it does seem that the Pill may actually protect against cancers of the ovary and womb lining, while possibly slightly increasing the risk of cancer of the cervix and, in younger women, cancer of the breast. However, research on this is not clear as yet. Anyone on the Pill should have regular smear tests to check for cancer of the cervix, which can be completely cured if diagnosed early on.

The health risks involved in taking the Pill are slight when compared to the risks of pregnancy and childbirth.

What should you do if you forget to take a Pill?

The combined Pill comes in packets of 21 or 28, and each Pill is labelled with the day of the week to help you to remember to take it. You should take your Pill at the same time each day for maximum effectiveness. The progestogen-only Pill should also be taken at the same time each day. It may be helpful to combine taking the Pill with cleaning your teeth in the morning or evening to help you establish a routine.

If you remember a forgotten Pill before the next one is due, take it straight away. If you forget to take a Pill for 12 hours or more, or you have severe diarrhoea or vomiting, you should take additional contraceptive precautions, such as using a condom, for the next seven days.

Does taking the Pill make it more difficult to get pregnant once contraception is stopped?

There is no evidence to suggest that former Pill-users find it any more difficult to get pregnant than those who have used other forms of contraception. One study showed that 75 per cent of the women who came off the Pill in order to get pregnant did so within three months, and a further 15 per cent did so within one year.

What is Emergency Contraception?

Occasionally called the 'morning after pill', this is a method which can be used if intercourse has taken place without contraception or if the usual method has failed, say in the event of a burst condom. It may also be prescribed to a woman after a sexual assault.

Two special doses of a pill are prescribed by a doctor, 12 hours apart. It works by altering the hormone balance either slowing down the egg in the fallopian tubes, or making the uterus wall unreceptive to a fertilized egg, or preventing ovulation if given early in the cycle. The next period may be earlier, or slightly later, than usual. It may make the woman feel sick, and if she is sick she will need more pills from a doctor. The pill can be given up to 72 hours after intercourse and is 96-99 per cent effective. A check-up with a doctor is necessary 3-4 weeks after treatment.

Can women be injected with contraceptive?

Yes, with a drug called Depo-Provera or Noristerat, which contains hormones of the progestogen type. An injection is needed every 8-12 weeks, depending on which drug is used. 'The Shot' or 'The Jab' is a virtually 100 per cent reliable contraceptive, but it often has a disruptive effect on a woman's menstrual cycle, making periods more frequent or even disappear altogether. Return of regular periods may be delayed for up to a year after the last injection.

What is the sponge?

The Today Sponge has been on the market in the UK for around seven years. It is impregnated with spermicide and the woman pushes it up into her vagina with a finger before sex. Neither partner should be able to feel it during lovemaking. The sponge must be left in place for six hours afterwards, but it can be left for up to 30 hours if necessary. It is removed quite simply by hooking a finger around a tape attached to the underside, and then it is discarded. It is 75-91 per cent effective.

What is the vaginal ring and how does it work?

This is a new method of contraception available on prescription from 1992. It combines the shape of the diaphragm with the contraceptive action of the progestogen-only Pill. The ring is made of soft, sterile silicone rubber and is 5cm/2 inches wide and 5mm/¼ inch thick. It is held in place by the vaginal muscles, and slowly releases into the body a low dose of the progestogen hormone levonorgestrel. The ring can be left in the vagina for three months before the hormone runs out and it needs renewing. If for any reason the ring comes out it must be replaced within three hours. It is not known exactly how effective the ring will turn out to be, but it is thought to be slightly less effective as a contraceptive method than the progestogen-only Pill. One disadvantage is that it may make some women's periods less regular.

Are hormone implants for women available yet?

This form of protection is likely to become available in 1992. Six small implants release a hormone into the bloodstream as does the vaginal ring, but it is not as intrusive. The implants are small, stick-like and pliable, and are inserted under the skin of the inner upper arm by your doctor or clinic in a simple, almost pain free, procedure. They cannot be seen. The effects will last for up to five years, and although the implants can be removed at any time, the body will not be free of the hormone for a short time afterwards, so this may not be the best method of contraception if you are contemplating pregnancy in the near future. Implants are reported to be highly reliable, more than 99%, although they may make periods less regular or disappear altogether. These side effects may settle down after several months.

What is the female condom?

This is a contraceptive that was developed over five years ago, and, after extensive trials, should be available from 1992.

It looks similar to an unrolled male condom, and lines the vagina; it has an inner ring which sits over the cervix and an outer ring which lies flat against the labia. The female condom is made of colourless odourless polyurethane. It is said to be stronger and more sensitive to heat than the latex used to make male condoms. It quickly reaches body temperature and should not be felt by either partner. The woman pushes the condom up inside her vagina before intercourse, and afterwards removes it and disposes of it. They come ready lubricated for easy insertion. Female condoms are made in one size only and will fit all women.

When is sterilization the best option?

Sterilization is an effective and permanent form of birth control. Couples or individuals who decide on this option are usually those who already have a family which they consider big enough, or in which the woman is past safe childbearing age and does not want to continue with the Pill or IUD, or those who have decided they never want children.

The partners are given counselling as a couple. Their motives are examined and the implications of sterilization explained to make absolutely sure that it is right for them. No one who wishes to be sterilized should assume that the operation can be reversed. Therefore, the couple will need to consider their future extremely seriously and if one partner is unsure they should not go ahead. They will need to ask themselves how they would feel if their relationship broke up, or if one of them died, or if one of their children died. If they still want to go ahead with the operation, the next thing to consider is which partner should be sterilized.

Are there any psychological problems associated with sterilization?

Sometimes there may be, and this is another reason why careful counselling is always necessary before the operation is agreed to. If a man has a hidden castration complex, which makes him fear that the operation will make him impotent, then obviously he should not be vasectomized. Men and women who cannot dissociate sexual pleasure from fertility could suffer from a lack of sexual drive after sterilization. However, the vast majority of couples find that the operation gives them a new sexual freedom because it releases them from the fear of pregnancy and the bother of taking precautions.

What happens when a man has a vasectomy?

A vasectomy is a very simple operation, more so than female sterilization. It can be performed under a local anaesthetic, and the patient can even watch what is happening – if he is not squeamish. He can be in and out of hospital within 15 or 20 minutes.

Male sterilization is called 'vasectomy' because the tubes from the testes to the penis – the vas deferens – are cut and tied, or cauterized, or sealed electrically or chemically, to prevent sperm from leaving the body. The surgeon makes a small incision in the scrotum – either one in the middle or one at either side – to perform the operation, and closes the incision or incisions with a couple of stitches. The stitches are made of a material that is naturally absorbed by the body, so there is no need to have them removed later.

What happens after the operation?

After the operation, the patient is advised not to do any heavy work, including lifting, for a few days, but otherwise he can lead a perfectly normal life. He may experience some temporary bruising and swelling, but his sex life can be resumed as soon as he feels comfortable.

Vasectomy is not immediately effective, as there will inevitably be some live sperm present in the system, but after up to 36 ejaculations these will all have been expelled. Two to four months after the operation, the man will be asked to return to hospital for a sperm check, and until the all-clear is given, he is advised to continue with whatever contraceptive he was using before the operation. Two clear semen tests (no sperm seen) are required before the vasectomy is considered to

have been successful.

Despite assurances to the contrary, many men worry that their sex lives will be affected by vasectomy. In fact, strength of erection, intensity of ejaculation and quantity of seminal fluid cannot be altered one way or the other by snipping the vas deferens; all that happens is that the fluid ejaculated no longer contains sperm. Sperm are still produced in the testes, but instead of being ejaculated, they are reabsorbed harmlessly into the body.

What happens during female sterilization?

The principle of female sterilization is to cut, cauterize or block the fallopian tubes so that sperm are prevented from reaching and fertilizing eggs. Female sterilization used always to involve major abdominal surgery, with a week's stay in hospital and a long and gradual recovery. But since the 1960s a new technique called laparoscopy has been developed, which makes the operation a relatively minor one; it can even be performed under a local anaesthetic if both doctor and patient are agreeable.

A very small tube is inserted through a tiny incision near the navel, and the gynaecologist pumps a harmless gas through it into the patient's abdomen. This pushes aside the intestines. He then inserts a viewing device called a laparoscope through the same incision: looking down it he can see the womb and the fallopian tubes. Through a second small incision near the pubic hair line he inserts a sterilizing instrument and performs the operation. It is all over within 15 minutes or so, and the patient can soon resume her normal life.

Although this new operation is obviously preferable to major surgery,

there may be medical reasons that make it inadvisable for some women.

While laparoscopy is now the most common method there are two other ways of performing female sterilization. Mini-laparotomy involves making a small cut in the abdomen, just below the bikini line, to reach the fallopian tubes. A general anaesthetic is necessary and a two-day stay in hospital. Occasionally the tubes are reached through a cut in the vagina.

As a method of contraception, is female sterilization an acceptable alternative to vasectomy?

No. Since the advent of laparoscopy, female sterilization has become a much less dangerous operation than it used to be. Vasectomy is a very much simpler operation with no lasting side-effects, and should be preferred every time as a method of contraception, unless there are medical reasons that dictate otherwise.

CELIBACY

Is celibacy bad for you?

Whether celibacy is chosen or not, the human sex drive cannot be suppressed totally, and most people without a partner find the need for sexual release through masturbation, whether this is frequent or rare. Some medical evidence is emerging that suggests that those with a good sex life live longer (perhaps because they are happy), and women who enjoy sex regularly seem to have less chance of suffering a heart attack. On the other hand, sex that is boring, monotonous, a duty or unwanted, has a depressing effect and can make a person feel degraded or useless, frustrated, and less than a full person.

131

If sex can make you feel either good or bad, then so can celibacy. Celibacy may be preferable to bad sex, but it can lead to a deep inner loneliness and frustration. If you are enduring enforced celibacy, try to balance it with as much friendly social contact as you need, and use masturbation to relieve sexual tension as it builds up. It is important to enjoy your body and not to neglect its needs.

On the plus side, a period of celibacy can help you to gather strength, independence and self-knowledge, and all of these qualities will bring added enjoyment to your next relationship.

Are there times when you should abstain from sex?

There are times when sex may be medically inadvisable, for example, if you have recently had a vaginal operation, a hernia operation or a hysterectomy. Some doctors may advise against sex for a pregnant woman with a history of miscarriages; you may be particularly vulnerable around the anniversary of your period for the first few months. In each of these cases where penetration is inadvisable, you can enjoy other forms of sex without harm. Sick and disabled people are often capable of enjoying a full and satisfying sex life.

Some people refrain from sex before an important occasion – say, a meeting or a sporting event – in the belief that sex and masturbation 'weaken' them. There is absolutely no medical evidence to support this belief, and any feeling of tiredness the following day is solely due to lack of sleep.

There is of course a potentially very serious problem if you are suffering from a sexually transmittable disease, such as VD, HIV, or AIDS (see pages

135-139). You will need to take every precaution against passing on the disease through sexual contact. Take your doctor's advice, or that of the special clinic you are attending. In cases of VD you may be told to abstain from sex for a period while taking medication, and then to use a condom for a further period. If you are HIV-positive you could put someone's life at risk by having sex with them, and this may mean restricting your sexual contact to partners who are also suffering from HIV or AIDS.

SEX DURING PREGNANCY

Is it safe to have sex right through pregnancy?

Yes. Unless you are told otherwise by your doctor, it is now considered perfectly safe to have sex during pregnancy for as long as you like. Towards the expected birth date, the woman's size may make many positions uncomfortable for her. Penetration may be easiest if she lies on her side and the man enters her from behind; oral sex and mutual masturbation should cause no problems. However, sex cannot trigger off labour unless the baby is due anyway, when the prostaglandins present in a man's semen can cause it to start.

The sex drive of some women decreases during pregnancy and immediately afterwards. This may be due to tiredness and stress, or to a hidden belief that it is not 'right' for a mother to enjoy sex. This problem will usually disappear of its own accord. In some women, the sex drive actually increases during the middle three months (the second trimester) of pregnancy, and some women even claim that their lovemaking is more satis-

fying than ever before. You can resume sex after childbirth as soon as it is comfortable to do so. Women who have had an episiotomy (in which the perineum is cut to facilitate birth), will probably feel sore for about three weeks. When you feel confident that your wound has healed, begin to re-establish your sex life again, taking it slowly and gently and using a lubricating jelly if necessary to prevent scar tissue causing any discomfort or pain. It is important to establish sexual contact with your partner as soon as you can, as he may be feeling that you are lavishing all your attention on the baby, and excluding him from your affections.

ABORTION

When is the right time to have an abortion?

Abortions are easiest performed before 12 weeks of pregnancy. After 16 weeks abortion via the vagina becomes more difficult and dangerous, and drugs are used to induce artificial labour (see following question). One per cent of abortions are performed after 20 weeks by major abdominal surgery. This is recommended only when severe complications have arisen late in the pregnancy.

What types of abortion are available?

The type of abortion will depend on the number of weeks a woman has been pregnant. Up to 12 weeks, vacuum suction is the preferred method. Under a general anaesthetic, the cervix is widened with dilating rods and a vacuum tube is inserted. The contents of the womb are removed in about five minutes. The patient may be allowed home on the

same day, but should take it easy for several days afterwards.

Dilation and evacuation (D & E) is recommended for patients from 13-24 weeks pregnant. In addition to the vacuum pump, surgical instruments are used to make sure that all fetal tissue is removed, and the operation takes about 30 minutes. Dilation and curettage (D & C) can be carried out between 12 and 16 weeks. The cervix is dilated as before and instruments are used to scrape out the womb. This takes around 20 minutes.

Amniocentesis is drug-induced labour. It is sometimes carried out on patients who are 15-24 weeks pregnant, and must be done in hospital. This is a very physically and emotionally distressing procedure and can take up to 12 hours. The patient is given an injection of prostaglandins, which make the uterus contract. Alternatively, a concentrated salt solution (saline) is introduced into the abdomen through a plastic tube, and labour starts several hours afterwards. The patient is given a local anaesthetic, and the fetus is expelled. A hospital stay of about two days is usually required. Any woman undergoing this operation will need professional counselling and the constant support of a close friend both before and afterwards.

Major surgery is required in a very small percentage of women from 15 to 24 weeks pregnant. Hysterotomy is an operation in which the fetus is removed through an incision in the abdomen and uterus – like Caesarian section. The stay in hospital will be a week or more. The physical and emotional effects of this operation can be extremely traumatic. The fetus may be born alive, but is not advanced enough to live.

What is the procedure for having an abortion?

First, your doctor will make sure that you are pregnant, and then he or she will discuss with you whether you really want an abortion. You have three alternatives: to have the baby and keep it; to have the baby and let it be fostered or adopted; or to terminate the pregnancy.

Many women have severe doubts about the morality of abortion, while others feel strongly that choice in the matter is a fundamental human right. However pro-abortion you may be, you will probably regard the operation with some misgivings. Women commonly worry that abortion will make them sterile or frigid. It won't, and there are rarely any physical complications, but in the weeks following the operation, be prepared to feel very depressed and sad, with feelings of inadequacy. During this difficult time, you will need the strong support of a friend, ideally of your partner, and you should make sure that you have this support before the operation, so that you can be taken to and from the clinic and looked after properly when you get home.

Due to a lack of NHS facilities, about half the abortions performed in Britain take place in private clinics. Make sure you know how much the operation will cost and sort out who will pay for it and how before the abortion.

What are the legal requirements for abortion?

Two doctors (probably your GP and a doctor at the clinic or hospital) must agree on one of the following:
1. Continuing the pregnancy involves greater risk to the woman's life than abortion.

Sexual Hygiene

Though the smell of a lover's sweat can have aphrodisiac qualities, clean bodies are generally more appetizing than dirty ones. Bathing is not always practicable or desirable, but you should always wash the genitals and anus before sex, to protect against infection, to increase the enjoyment of your partner and to give self confidence. Soap and water are all that is needed. Deodorants and perfumes kill the body's delightful natural scents, and they also taste extremely unpleasant. Vaginal deodorants can be positively harmful, destroying the micro-organisms in the vagina that protect against disease.

Anything that is inserted in the anus should be washed afterwards, particularly if it is then to be inserted in the vagina, as anal sex carries the highest risk of infection. Sometimes, washing or showering together after sex is part of the enjoyment, but generally, relaxing or sleeping together is far preferable to leaping off to the bathroom, which breaks the intimate mood and can be hurtful to the other person.

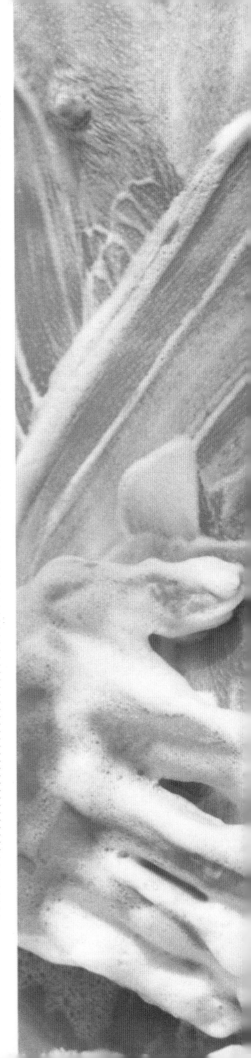

2. Continuing the pregnancy involves greater risk of injury to the woman's physical or mental health than abortion.

3. Continuing the pregnancy involves greater risk of injury to the physical or mental health of existing children in the family than abortion.

4. There is a substantial risk that the child will be born seriously deformed (e.g. by spina bifida or mongolism).

How long does it take to recover physically from an abortion?

This really depends on the type of operation you have. If you have had amniocentesis or hysterotomy, your doctor and a professional counsellor will be there to help you find a route to recovery. After an earlier abortion, be prepared to take some rest and do not engage in any strenuous activity for at least a week. For two to three weeks, you should not use tampons or douching, or have sexual intercourse. At this time you are very prone to infection, and any unusual symptoms, such as heavy bleeding, vaginal discharge, cramps or nausea should be reported to your doctor.

Go to your doctor for a check-up around a week after the abortion, and start using contraception again at this time too.

AIDS

What is AIDS?

The letters AIDS stand for Acquired Immune Deficiency Syndrome, and the disease is caused by the human immunodeficiency virus, known as HIV. Once it is inside the body, this virus invades the white blood cells, which normally fight off disease, then it multiplies and destroys them. It also

How to Avoid AIDS

- Always use a condom.
- Avoid anal sex.
- Don't share toothbrushes, razors or any other instrument that might transfer blood from cuts or abrasions.
- If you are haemophiliac, avoid pregnancy, until you are certain that both partners are clear of the virus, as HIV is transmitted to the fetus.

breeds inside the brain. Three to four years normally elapse between infection with HIV and any subsequent development of AIDS.

As the body's defences are depleted, the AIDS patient is increasingly likely to contract diseases that a healthy body would normally ward off, and so rare forms of cancer and pneumonia develop. Sometimes AIDS patients are attacked by several infections at once, such as candida, herpes and TB. At the same time, the brain may succumb to increasingly severe dementia.

Somewhere between one in ten and one in three of those infected with HIV are likely to develop AIDS. As yet there is no cure for AIDS. The drug Retrovir may buy time for the AIDS sufferer, but it has unpleasant side-effects. AIDS usually progresses through various infections and stages of increasing debility to the eventual death of the sufferer.

Can AIDS be transmitted by casual social contact?

No. Infection is caused when the virus enters the body through an injection or a cut or abrasion on the skin, or through the mucous membranes lining the mouth, vagina or rectum. The rectum is especially vulnerable because its lining is so thin and delicate. During anal intercourse, the receptive male is particularly at risk from infected semen because the male body is not biologically adapted to dealing with semen in the way that the female body is.

There is no proof that HIV can be transmitted by mouth-to-mouth kissing, though oral contact with the penis or anus of an infected person would be dangerous. Generally, most doctors agree that HIV is not even likely to be transmitted by a single sexual encounter with an infected person, but that repeated sexual contact with one or more infected people

AIDS: Symptoms and Testing

Three or four years, or longer, can elapse between contracting HIV and developing AIDS. During this time, anyone who is HIV-positive may unknowingly infect other people.

Some people with HIV have no symptoms, but others develop something like glandular fever shortly after infection. Once this has cleared up, the patient may have no other indication of the virus for several years.

The first signs of AIDS itself are usually permanently swollen lymph glands and skin infections,

followed by bouts of fever, diarrhoea and oral thrush. This stage of the disease is known as AIDS-related complex, or ARC, and it precedes full-blown AIDS.

You are most likely to be at risk from AIDS if you are homosexual; if your partner is a bisexual male; if one of you has had casual homosexual or heterosexual relationships, particularly in New York, Edinburgh or Central or East Africa; or if one of you is an intravenous drug user. However, any exchange of semen or blood can carry the risk of infection.

A blood test can confirm whether or not you are HIV-positive. The drawback of the test is that it is not always conclusive. HIV antibodies may take weeks or months to develop in the blood, so a test may show negative after recent infection. If it shows positive, a second test will be carried out to verify the result. Not everyone who is HIV-positive will go on to develop full-blown AIDS, but everyone who takes the test should have some counselling to prepare themselves for the implications of a positive result.

certainly does put the individual gravely at risk.

During her work with AIDS sufferers, the Princess of Wales has tried to demonstrate that ordinary human contact with them poses no risk whatsoever. There is absolutely no need to follow the hysterical practice of cutting AIDS sufferers off from society 'to protect the majority', because most individuals (except those who have been infected via contaminated blood transfusions) have to make a conscious decision before they put themselves at risk.

How do you catch AIDS?

The virus is present in body fluids, primarily semen and blood. It may also be present in saliva, though research indicates that saliva seems to present little risk. Having anal intercourse with an infected partner is the most likely way of catching AIDS, and 80 per cent of British cases so far have been male homosexuals.

The second most common way of contracting the disease is through infected blood. Almost a quarter of Britain's haemophiliac population now carry HIV because they have been injected with the clotting agent collected from infected blood. (Haemophiliacs are born without the blood-clotting factor, and can suffer severe bruising from a minor injury, and bleed to death from a cut unless they receive the clotting factor from donated blood.)

HIV in the blood may also be transmitted on infected needles, and drug addicts are the third most highly at risk group of the population.

Of course, you do not have to be homosexual or promiscuous, a drug addict or a haemophiliac to become HIV positive. Heterosexuals are also

at risk and may be infected by a partner in a steady relationship who has contracted the disease from an ex-partner, say. Therefore when embarking on any new relationship, it is safest to wear a condom.

SEXUALLY TRANSMITTED DISEASES

Can STDs be caught from lavatory seats?

No, this is extremely unlikely. The organisms that transmit STDs thrive in warm moist places, such as the mouth, anus and vagina, and are passed on, as their name implies, by oral, genital or anal sex. In rare cases, they may be passed on by kissing. The organisms die within moments of being outside their natural environment, but it is just about conceivable that they could be transmitted on, say, a towel shared immediately after sex.

If you suspect you may have a sexually transmitted disease, you should see your doctor or clinic straight away. You can find the telephone number of your nearest clinic by looking up 'special clinic', 'venereal disease' or 'VD' in the telephone directory, or by phoning your local hospital or Citizens' Advice Bureau. You will be tested as quickly as possible, and if the test is positive, you will be advised to contact your recent sexual partners, as they too may need treatment. Avoid sex until you are clear of the disease.

What are the symptoms of gonorrhoea?

The bacterium gonococcus, which causes gonorrhoea, cannot survive outside the body and is transmitted only by sexual intercourse, and never

on toilet seats or towels. In men the urethra, along which urine passes from the bladder, is infected, and there is sometimes pain on urinating and a thick discharge from the penis within a week after infection. In homosexual men the rectum may be infected, with the possibility of irritation and discharge from the anus.

In women the cervix, urethra and rectum can be infected, and, as with men, there may be discharge and pain on urinating. If infection spreads to the uterus there is a 10 per cent chance that the fallopian tubes may be blocked, causing sterility. Often, however, there are no symptoms in either men or women.

The treatment for gonorrhoea is usually a single dose of antibiotics such as penicillin, with a check-up afterwards to make sure the infection has cleared. If gonorrhoea is not diagnosed and treated, serious complications can develop. Men may suffer epididymitis – pain and swelling in the testicles; women may suffer peritonitis – inflammation of the membranes of the abdomen. Both sexes could develop gonococcal septicaemia, an infection of the bloodstream with skin rashes and arthritis. Sterility can result in both sexes. Pregnant women with gonorrhoea may pass it on to their babies, who can be born with conjunctivitis, an acute inflammation of the eyes. Complications are, however, relatively rare nowadays.

What is the most common STD?

This is NSU, or non-specific urethritis, also called NGU, non-gonococcal urethritis. The symptoms are as described in the box. The treatment is usually a two-week course of antibiotics for anyone who has had contact with an infected person. During treatment, patients are asked to give up alcohol, as this can bring about a recurrence of the symptoms. Complications can occur, and these are similar to those for gonorrhoea, but fortunately early diagnosis and treatment can prevent these.

It is possible for a man to be periodically reinfected with NGU without changing his sex partner, and no explanation has so far been put forward for this. However, both partners will need treatment each time NGU manifests itself.

Has syphilis been eradicated?

No, but it is fortunately quite rare in Britain today. It affects women less than men, and its main victims are male homosexuals. Symptoms appear between 10 days and 12 weeks after infection. In the primary stage of the disease a small hard sore or chancre appears on the penis, vagina or rectum. It is painless and usually disappears very quickly. A few weeks later, in the secondary stage, the patient is feverish, with swollen glands and itching skin. The disease is curable with antibiotics, but if for some reason it should not be treated, serious complications will develop many years later. Until the advent of antibiotics, tertiary syphilis used to be quite common, with patients eventually suffering from dementia and dying a slow, agonizing death.

What is genital herpes, and is there an effective treatment for it?

Genital herpes is a viral infection transmitted through sexual intercourse. It is very similar to the other sort of herpes, which causes cold sores, and can also be caught by having oral sex with someone who has active cold sores. The symptoms are itching, pain

in the groin, discomfort on urinating and fever, followed by the appearance of painful red blisters on the vulva or penis, which burst to form ulcers. After about 10 days the symptoms disappear and the patient appears to be cured. But the infection is only lying dormant and may recur at any time, particularly when the patient is under stress. There is as yet no treatment for this disease, though the drug Acyclovir relieves symptoms and reduces the duration of attacks. Doctors may also prescribe bed rest, with paracetamol for the pain and a saline bath for the infected area.

During the dormant phase of the disease, it is safe to have sex without infecting one's partner, but it is impossible to predict when the next attack may occur, so the risk of infection remains. If the infection is active at the end of a pregnancy, a Caesarian section may be performed to prevent the baby becoming infected in the birth canal.

Genital herpes is a very painful and distressing disease, which has reached epidemic proportions in America. The good news is that it does sometimes burn itself out, and that the prospect of an eventual cure looks promising.

Are genital warts serious?

No: they are unpleasant but painless and can be treated quite easily. They are small lumps that appear on the penis, vulva or anus and are mildly contagious. The treatment involves either painting the warts with a preparation called podophyllin, or freezing them off with liquid nitrogen. An association has been identified between genital warts and cervical cancer, so it is important to get rid of them as soon as possible, and to have regular cervical smears.

The Symptoms of STD

Very often there are no symptoms at all of STD, but if your partner has one of these diseases, or you have a sexual relationship with someone who is promiscuous, then a check-up is essential. If symptoms do manifest themselves, they are likely to take the form of a discharge from the vagina, penis or anus, or itching or soreness around the genitals or anus, or a lump or rash on the genitals, anus or mouth.

THRUSH

Does thrush mean that a woman or her partner has been unfaithful?

No, not necessarily. Thrush is a fungal infection that develops in certain conditions in the vagina. It is sometimes linked to taking the Pill, and if it recurs frequently, a different method of contraception may be advisable. A man may carry thrush, though he usually manifests no symptoms. Thrush causes vaginal soreness and itching, and a thick white discharge. The doctor will probably prescribe anti-fungal cream, to be used by both partners, and vaginal pessaries, though oral treatments are available too. Some women find that natural yoghurt in the vagina is effective. Avoid hot baths, and wearing tights, tight jeans and nylon knickers.

139

FEMALE SEXUALITY

Does the G-spot really exist?

Named after its discoverer, Ernst Grafenberg, there is still a controversy about whether the G-spot actually exists or not, but many women claim that stimulating a place about 5cm/2 inches inside the vagina towards the front of the body gives them intense pleasure, and no one can say better than that.

The G-spot is said to be the female equivalent of the male prostate gland, which is situated about 5cm/2 inches up the rectum towards the front of the body. Stimulation of both these places can lead to orgasm in some cases. Some women have even found that they ejaculate a fluid if they have an orgasm by stimulation of the G-spot, and researchers in Canada and the United States claim that the composition of this fluid is remarkably similar to the secretion of the prostate gland.

How do you find the G-spot?

If you doubt the existence of the G-spot, you can try to find it yourself. The easiest way to reach it is probably with your own or your partner's finger, but there are also positions for intercourse in which the penis should stimulate the sensitive area. Rear-entry is best, particularly with the man on top and a pillow beneath your hips, so that the penis presses against the front wall of the vagina.

What exactly causes a woman to have periods?

Women have periods, or menstruate (from the Latin *mensis*, month), from the age of puberty to the menopause,

Sex Questions and Answers

i.e. from around age 12 to age 49. This means around 480 periods in a lifetime. Each month, the lining of the womb is enriched with blood vessels to receive a fertilized egg that may develop into a baby. However, if no egg is fertilized or implanted, the lining of the womb breaks up. A change in the woman's hormonal balance causes the disintegration of the womb lining, and bleeding occurs. The length of the menstrual cycle varies, usually being between 21 and 36 days, with an average of 28 days. Bleeding lasts from one to eight days with an average of five.

Many women find that periods bring pain or discomfort, and may be accompanied by premenstrual tension beforehand. About one woman in five has prolonged or heavy periods. Heavy loss of iron-rich blood can cause anaemia, and this explains why women are much more likely to be anaemic than men.

What can be done to regulate prolonged and heavy periods?

A very good way of alleviating this problem is to go on the Pill. It has helped countless women worldwide to get rid of period pain, to lighten the menstrual flow and to shorten the length of periods to only a few days. For other information about taking the Pill, see pp. 127, 129.

Is it alright to have sexual intercourse during menstruation?

Yes, it is perfectly safe. Some women feel at their most sexy just before and during their period, and it would be a shame to deny these feelings. If your partner does not know already, it is courteous to let him know that you are menstruating before he finds out for himself. Some men are squeamish about blood, and may lose interest in

sex if there is a lot of it, which could hurt your feelings. You can protect the bed by lying on a towel, and if you feel it necessary you could temporarily stem the flow by using a diaphragm, though contraception should not normally be needed at this time.

Is it normal to suffer period pains?

Unfortunately, yes. There are no statistics available for the UK, but in the United States it has been estimated that at least half the women of child-bearing age suffer from dysmenorrhoea, as period pains are called. One survey in Sweden revealed that 90 per cent suffered from menstrual pain. The pain can be excrutiating, and sadly this fact is not appreciated by many men, including some male doctors. There is a wide range of symptoms, including abdominal cramps just before the onset of the period, intense suffering throughout its duration, with cramps, bladder distress, painful breasts, abdominal distension, pelvic soreness, backache, nausea, vomiting, headaches and fainting. Needless to say, there is also likely to be irritability and depression, and some women are unable to pursue their normal lives for one or two days. Dysmenorrhoea usually diminishes after childbirth.

Research has shown that dysmenorrhoea has a biological cause: women who suffer from it produce large quantities of prostaglandins at the time of menstruation, and these cause the symptoms described above. Now treatment is available from your doctor in the form of a drug called a prostaglandin inhibitor. In trials, this drug has been shown to cure 70–90 per cent of dysmenorrhoeic women of all their symptoms, and to allow 70 per cent of those who had to take to their beds at the onset of their periods to lead a normal life.

Is vaginal discharge normal?

All women have some natural vaginal discharge. It is odourless and colourless, although it may dry to a white or yellow stain on your pants. When you are sexually aroused, the discharge will increase, and, of course, if your partner has ejaculated inside you, semen may seep from your vagina over a number of hours.

If the discharge is more copious, or looks or smells different, it should be investigated. The first thing to ask yourself is whether you have forgotten to remove a tampon or diaphragm. If you have, then it may have caused a slight infection. Remove it straight away and the discharge should clear up soon afterwards. If it does not, you should see a doctor.

If the discharge is white and curd-like, you may have thrush. Other symptoms are irritation of the vagina and the surrounding area, painful and

Points to Watch Around the Onset of Menstruation

In addition to the symptoms described above, every woman should be aware that she may suffer some of the following just before and during her period:

● **Skin problems.** Spots, acne and greasy skin are most likely to be troublesome at this time. You should be careful to eat a diet that is low in fat, and as much fresh fruit as you can.

● **Fluctuations in appetite.** Although some women lose their appetite completely, others may feel immensely hungry and can often eat far more than they would normally.

● **The urge to drink.** Women who like alcohol are particularly prone to drinking bouts at this time of the month, and with sorry consequences, because alcohol is broken down more slowly at menstruation and therefore accumulates in the bloodstream. If you are surprised at the severity of your hangover in the morning, consult the calendar, and make a note to drink only moderately at this stage of your cycle.

● **Headaches.** Women who experience severe headaches and migraine are substantially more likely to do so around the time of menstruation, and especially if they are on the Pill.

● **Fluid retention.** Your fingers and ankles may swell, you may feel bloated, and fluid in the eyes and gums may make the wearing of contact lenses and false teeth uncomfortable.

143

What to Do if You Suffer From PMT

● **Keep a record of your symptoms, such as headache and tension, in a menstrual diary. As far as you can, avoid planning demanding events on days when you are likely to be feeling below your best. Take as much rest on these days as possible.**

● **Discuss your feelings with your partner, and with your doctor, and ask for support from the first and treatment from the second. Your doctor may suggest a course of progesterone.**

● **If PMT affects your work, confide in your employer. Try not to take on too much demanding work at crucial times of the month.**

● **Eat a healthy diet rich in wholegrains, fresh fruit and vegetables. Avoid too many salty foods and limit your fluid intake from the middle of your cycle. Foods rich in potassium, such as beans, potatoes, fish and nuts, will help combat fluid retention.**

frequent urination, and pain on intercourse. See p. 139 for advice.

If the discharge is yellowish with an offensive smell, you may have trichomonal vaginitis. This is a common vaginal infection like thrush, and its symptoms are similar, but at their worst just after menstruation. As the infection can be passed to and received from your partner, both of you will have to take a course of tablets (as will any other sexual partners of either of you). Consult your doctor.

If you have an abnormal discharge and pain in the lower abdomen, you should see your doctor without delay. It is possibly due to a pelvic infection, and, if it remains untreated, could result in sterility.

Discharge may also be caused by one of a number of sexually transmitted diseases (see p. 139).

What is PMT?

Premenstrual tension affects around 40 per cent of women, who suffer symptoms of tiredness, irritability and depression around the onset of their periods. In some women the symptoms are hardly apparent, but others almost reach breaking point, cannot cope with the normal stresses of everyday life, and may become aggressive or hysterical. A woman suffering PMT may feel insecure, inadequate, unable to stop crying, incapable of making decisions or of concentrating, and uninterested in sex, eating or enjoying herself. A loss of insight often blinds her to the fact that her depression is hormonal and will pass, and in severe cases, suicidal feelings may develop. Surveys in Britain, France and the United States have shown that women are more likely to commit crimes during or just before menstruation than at other times in their cycle.

These symptoms are caused by hormonal imbalance in the critical days before the period. Research has shown that PMT-sufferers tend to have lower than normal levels of progesterone and higher than normal levels of oestrogen; the discrepancy is felt on those days when the hormone levels are changing very rapidly.

Why does PMT sometimes start after childbirth?

Some women begin to suffer from PMT after childbirth, although they have never suffered from it before. This is because the ovaries stop supplying progesterone during pregnancy and this function is taken over by the placenta (afterbirth). After the baby is born, the ovaries have to start producing progesterone again, and it may take them a while to reach normal production levels. A deficiency in the hormone can lead to classic symptoms of PMT, such as tiredness, irritability and depression.

What causes bleeding between periods?

Bleeding between periods or breakthrough bleeding (metrorrhagia) is experienced by 10 per cent of women on the Pill, at the time of ovulation. It usually occurs during the first few months of taking the Pill, especially the mini-Pill, as it takes time for the hormones in the drug to regulate ovulation. Women newly fitted with the coil (see p. 127) often experience breakthrough bleeding, or it may be due to fibroids (benign lumps growing in the womb). Consult your doctor.

What causes periods to stop altogether?

The most obvious cause is pregnancy, and this would be the first thing the

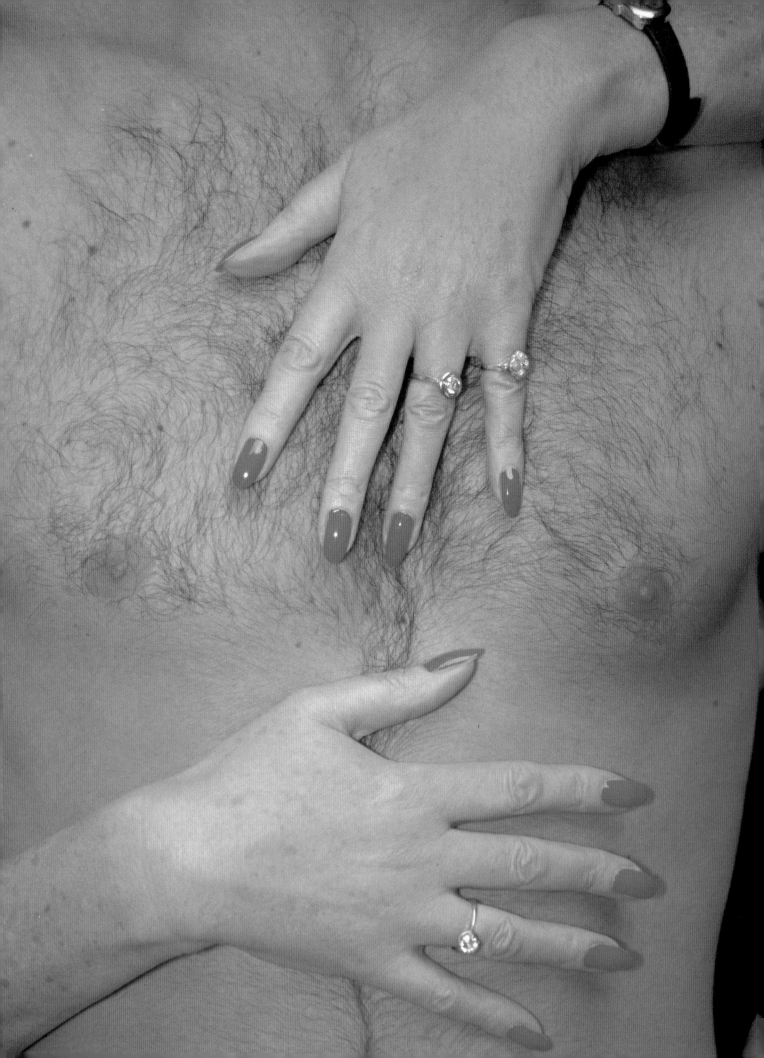

doctor would investigate. Other causes of amenorrhoea are severe stress and a dramatic change in weight – either gain or loss. Some women who stop taking the Pill have no periods for up to a year afterwards. Amenorrhoea may also be a side-effect of certain chronic illnesses. Although you may welcome the absence of periods, unless of course you hope to get pregnant, it is advisable to consult your doctor. Another cause of amenorrhoea, albeit it more rare, is a high level of physical exercise and subsequent weight loss. Many women athletes, especially distance runners, experience this, although their periods usually return quite quickly when they reduce their level of training.

What happens at the menopause?
The menopause is when periods stop and a woman is no longer able to bear children. Ageing causes the ovaries to stop releasing eggs at around 49 (average age). Every woman is born with millions of egg follicles in her ovaries, and around 480 of these are released during a lifetime's ovulation. At the menopause the remaining egg follicles degenerate, and there are lower levels of oestrogen and progesterone circulating in the bloodstream. The reduction in hormone levels is responsible for the sometimes unpleasant symptoms associated with the menopause (see the box below). Periods may stop suddenly, never to resume, or they may become gradually sparser, and further and further apart. If there is any irregular bleeding, bleeding after intercourse or very heavy bleeding, you should see your doctor for a check up straight away, as this is abnormal.

The risk of cancer of the womb or cervix is quite high at this age and any untoward symptoms should be checked out immediately.

What is hormone replacement therapy?
Hormone replacement therapy (HRT) is a treatment of the female hormones oestrogen and progestogen given to menopausal women to cure them of all the symptoms listed in the box below. They can be given by mouth or via an implant under the skin. In the case of vaginal dryness, a hormone cream will be prescribed which should be applied nightly in the vagina for as long as the problem persists. The vagina will return to its normal healthy state and lovemaking will no longer cause discomfort. The treatment can be reduced gradually once

Symptoms of the Menopause

Note that all these symptoms may be cured by hormone replacement therapy (HRT).

● The most frequently experienced symptom is hot flushes. Sudden rushes of heat, followed by cold and profuse sweating, may occur over a period of two to three years, particularly at night. They are not usually accompanied by blushing, and no one should notice them but yourself. Vitamin E, contained in wheatgerm oil, may help. Try to avoid embarrassing or stressful situations, as these tend to exacerbate hot flushes.

● Sometimes there is a loosening of the vaginal and pelvic muscles with the result that you may find a little urine is released if you cough or laugh. You can exercise your muscles to bring them back into condition. Clench and release them while you are sitting relaxed in a chair or lying in bed; or when you urinate, practise stopping and starting the flow of urine.

● The vaginal tissue, like the skin elsewhere on your body, may become dry and thin. Use a good moisturizer and a body lotion, and if your vagina is sore or dry when you have sex, use a lubricating jelly. Your doctor might also prescribe vaginal hormone cream.

● The disruption to the hormones sometimes causes a growth of facial hair, which may be distressing. A beauty salon can remove this permanently with electrolysis, or you can try a depilatory cream or bleaching, although you should be careful to do a skin test first, as your skin may react adversely. Odd hairs can be removed with tweezers.

● Expect some emotional disruption due to your changing hormone balance. You may feel depressed or anxious, inadequate and tearful. Once the menopause is over, however, a new serenity will descend on you, but you may decide not to wait for it, and to consider a course of hormone replacement therapy instead.

the symptoms have passed, but it may also be continued safely for 10 or even 20 years. Some doctors recommend taking it for life to avoid osteoporosis, a gradual crumbling of the bones which may result eventually in 'dowager's hump', and affects many elderly women in varying degrees.

Does the menopause mean the end of a woman's sex life?

Not at all. A woman may have a sex life for as long as she enjoys it, and the menopause should have no long-term effect on enjoyment. You may experience some discomfort during penetration because of thinning of the vaginal walls, and menopausal depression may put you off sex for a while, but both these problems can be cured by HRT and an understanding partner. When periods stop and there is no further risk of childbirth, many women feel a new rush of sexual potency and take new pleasure in making love.

What should a woman do to experience orgasms, if she never or rarely has them?

The best way of teaching yourself to orgasm is by getting to know your own body, its anatomy and its reactions, and by teaching yourself to masturbate (see p. 86). Once you have learned how to arouse yourself, you will be in a better position to teach your partner how to do it for you.

There is a great deal of pressure on a woman to have orgasms, and the more she feels this pressure, the less likely she is to climax. The more you concentrate on trying and the more worried you are, the less spontaneous you will become, and the result will probably be disappointment and feelings of inadequacy for both of you. See Shyness and inhibitions (p. 23),

Intimacy (p. 48), The female orgasm (p. 38) and Understanding a woman's feelings (p. 52).

Is it possible for a woman to be 'too small' for penetration?

Some women find penetration painful, and a small minority are unable to achieve it with their partners. This distressing condition is almost always due to tension. To enjoy sex you need to be feeling both relaxed and aroused. If your partner does not know how to make you feel good, you are probably worried that he will hurt you, and this makes your muscles tense. If he tries to penetrate you immediately and comes quickly before you are naturally lubricated, sex will not be a very fulfilling experience for you. He is probably as inexperienced and nervous as you are, and has no idea how to please a woman. Show him what you like and get him to take things much more slowly and gently until your bodies get to know and trust each other.

In a very few women who are unable to receive penetration, the hymen – the membrane of skin that covers the lower end of the vagina in a virgin – is found to be abnormally tough. The problem is unusual nowadays, especially as many young women wear tampons before they lose their virginity. Let your doctor examine you; if there is a problem with the hymen it can be put right with a simple operation. Under a general anaesthetic, a gynaecologist will make a small incision in the membrane, and a perfectly normal vagina will be discovered underneath. But if penetration is difficult, it is more likely that your doctor will tell you how to stretch the opening yourself, by using lubricating jelly and gently inserting your fingers into your vagina.

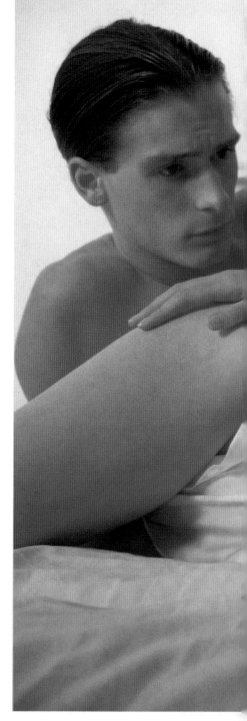

Can sex therapy help?

Sex therapy can be an enormous help if both parties truly wish to keep and improve their relationship. If the fire has gone out of it, then no amount of counselling of any sort will bring it back, though it may well help you to reach the difficult and painful decision to go your separate ways.

Sex therapy usually takes the form of very gentle discussion of your particular situation and difficulties. Your

problems will be explored over a number of weeks or months, during which you and your partner will be advised not to try intercourse at all. Instead, you will be given a programme to follow, which will help you to very slowly get to know each other's bodies, without preconceptions. For instance, you might be asked to just stroke each other gently with the fingertips, to concentrate on the sensation of skin on skin. You will probably be given exercises to strengthen your vaginal muscles, and move on to learning how to please yourself.

Over a number of weeks, you will learn how to relax and enjoy your body, and gradually to share your pleasure with your partner. Many people find themselves ready for genital contact and full sexual intercourse before it appears on the programme agreed with their counsellor, and this shows that counselling has worked.

Sex therapy can be successful only if it takes place with the full support and agreement of your partner, whether he or she has therapy too or not, and if you both agree to stick to the programme the counsellor devises for you. People who stick to the rules often feel a burden is lifted from them as all the problems they have wrestled with are removed, and relaxation, pleasure and excitement are slowly introduced into their lives.

What is to be done if a woman is not interested in sex?

We are all sexual beings and have the potential to be interested in sex all our lives. If a woman is interested in sex but afraid of it, there is hope that the relationship will improve (see above). However, if she is bored with sex, it may be nearer the truth to say that she is not interested in her partner. If so, then no matter how good his understanding of the female body and its responses, he will get no fire from her. The same of course applies to men who lack interest.

Even though it may be technically similar, there is nothing less like good, exciting and fulfilling sex than sex for the sake of it, just to keep a relationship together. Masturbation can be more fun. If you are in this situation, it is probably time to ask yourself whether you intend to remain in it, and to start talking with your partner about the possibilities for improvement, if they exist, or for parting, if they don't. Alternatively, you may come to the conclusion, independently or together, that you prefer the status quo to the trauma of splitting up. In this case you should be prepared for the possibility of the frustrated partner seeking sexual satisfaction outside the relationship.

What can a man do to educate a clumsy lover?

Men often complain that women treat their bodies as if they were machines. Pull this lever and pleasure will result. In fact, the entire male body can become an erogenous zone if you both allow this to happen. Men derive a great deal of erotic pleasure out of massage, after all. It is all a matter of allowing sensitivity to develop between you, and this takes experience.

The problem of having a clumsy lover is one that can be resolved together, as it usually stems from nervousness or inexperience, or both. Clumsiness comes from not being aware of your partner's needs for gentleness, and from a lack of confidence in yourself, and in your ability to give pleasure. If your lover is clumsy and doesn't know it, you can either tell her or show her which caresses feel good, or you can ask her to show you what she likes first, then reverse the process, to make it feel more equal. Educating a clumsy lover who wants to improve her technique and give you pleasure can be very exciting for both of you. Tolerating her fumblings will only create resentment.

MALE SEXUALITY

Is there such a thing as the male menopause?

Since menopause means the end of having periods, and men don't have periods, there is technically no such thing. Unlike women, men do not suffer a sudden drop in the production of their sex hormones in mid-life, and healthy men can father children well into old age. The decline in testosterone production is very gradual, and begins at around 40. The phrase 'male menopause' refers more to a state of mind that some men experience in their 40s or 50s, in which they feel self-doubt and depression and wonder why life seems to have 'passed them by'. The way out of the problem is to come to terms with the reality of the situation, which is probably by no means as bleak as it seems. Thinking hard about the direction one's life is going in is no bad thing and may lead to reorientation towards new goals.

What is wrong if a man can't get an erection?

Most men suffer from this problem at some time in their lives, particularly if they have had a lot to drink. It is important not to confuse temporary disability with impotence. The word 'impotence' is very depressing to any man and damaging to any relationship, because it suggests that the problem will recur, and the suggestion makes recurrence more likely.

In a small number of cases lack of erection is a physical problem, but in the majority of healthy males the reason for it is purely psychological. The exception is when the foreskin is so tight that erection becomes painful; this conditions the man to be incapable of erection, and circumcision will probably be recommended to put the problem right.

Psychological reasons for lack of erection are many and various. Even though he may want sex, a man who feels negative emotions, such as guilt or fear, in the presence of a particular woman, will not be able to penetrate her. If this is an extramarital relationship, he may very well be afraid of his wife finding out, or of making his partner pregnant, or of catching a disease from her which he would then transmit to his wife.

In some cases, men are impotent with their wives, but can manage penetration easily with other women. The reason for this is the idea that a man's wife, like his mother, is sexless and sacred – some men even refer to their wives as 'mother'. Just as it would not be right for a man to have sex with his mother, so sex with his wife seems in some way to sully her. Sex with

The Prostate Gland

This is a gland about the size of a walnut situated at the opening of the bladder. Women do not have a prostate; the female equivalent is the G-spot (see p. 141). The function of the prostate is to produce a secretion that forms part of the seminal fluid. With age, the prostate gland enlarges; this is perfectly normal, but it can cause problems, because the urethra, through which urine leaves the body, passes directly through the prostate and can become restricted as the gland enlarges. This makes it dificult to pass urine. If it becomes impossible to pass urine (acute retention), emergency treatment is necessary.

Three in four prostate patients do not find the enlarged gland to be too much of a problem, and it should not affect sex. They are advised to cut down on fluid intake and to urinate frequently, as this will lessen the chances of acute retention. Of those who do need an operation, some will have a transurethral resection (TUR), which means that bits of the prostate will be scraped away to make the urethral passage larger. This is done under general anaesthetic by pushing a minute telescope fitted with a cutting device up the urethra. In other cases, the whole gland will be removed. This is no longer the dangerous operation it used to be, though the patient may need to spend a couple of weeks in hospital and relax for a month at home.

Prostatectomy, as the operation is called, will not affect sexual performance. However, there may be an apparent lack of ejaculation, caused by seminal fluid entering the bladder instead of passing out of the penis through the urethra. This is called retrograde ejaculation. The semen will make the urine cloudy, but this is not a problem, and the ability to orgasm is not affected. After prostatectomy, fertility will probably cease, but the operation is not usually performed before the mid-50s, and by this age most men have completed their families. Your doctor may well advise you to continue with contraception, however, if your partner is of childbearing age.

other women, however, whom he has not put on the pedestal of holy matrimony, seems perfectly alright. Sometimes a man who subconsciously mixes his wife up with his mother thinks of sex as dirty and degrading. He is only able to penetrate women who seem to him degraded by sex, such as prostitutes.

Quite often, a man's first time with a new partner leaves him with a crushing sense of inadequacy because he can't maintain an erection. This may be because of a feeling of being overwhelmed by a situation he has wanted to be in for so long, and now feels incapable of living up to. A tactful and loving partner can help him to feel at ease and to regain his confidence.

A man may also fail to get an erection if there is unresolved hostility or anger in the relationship, or if his partner has criticised his lovemaking in a hurtful way. Too often people forget that sex is a sharing of erotic feelings that grows out of the rest of life; it is impossible to have good sex, and sometimes impossible to have sex at all, if the rest of the relationship is in disarray.

What should a woman do if her partner can't get an erection?

If your partner can't get an erection with you even through self-stimulation, the important thing is not to overreact. Most men find this a humiliating experience, and though it would be impossible, and unwise, to ignore it, patience and not criticism is what is called for. The first thing to do is to take off the pressure. If you try to help by stimulating your partner's penis when an erection seems out of the question, you will only succeed in making him feel more inadequate. If, on the other hand, you break the mood and concentrate for a while on something other than sex, just cuddling and talking about whatever comes into your head, the problem may resolve itself of its own accord.

If lack of erection recurs, then talk to your partner about why you think it is happening. Often he may be blocking out the reason, while it seems perfectly obvious to you. Suggest that you abstain from intercourse for a while: if he is not expected to perform,

151

he won't be in danger of feeling a failure, and his confidence can be restored gradually. This is more likely to happen if you make him feel that you want him, but wait until he is ready to come to you. You can give him plenty of affection in other ways. For instance, you could show him how much you appreciate his body by giving him a massage (see p. 94).

A man who consistently fails to get an erection with a woman he would like to have sex with is right to consider himself impotent with that woman. Sex therapy could provide the answer. A counsellor would discuss the possible causes of impotence, while setting out a programme of recovery. Over the following weeks, the man might be encouraged to masturbate alone, and to restrict sexual activity with his partner to caressing and non-genital massage. He might then be advised to progress to masturbating in front of his partner, and to mutual masturbation, before attempting intercourse again.

The Stop-start Technique for Delaying Ejaculation

This is a sequence of exercises designed by Dr James Semans to help the large number of men who ejaculate immediately they enter or touch a woman's vagina with the penis, or even before. The aim of the exercises is to learn to keep yourself below the point at which ejaculation seems inevitable for as long as possible. The first three steps of Dr Semans' exercise can be practised by men who do not have a partner. In themselves, they will help you gain a greater measure of control. For the final four steps you will need the cooperation of a partner.

● Step one. Masturbate with a dry hand. Avoid fantasizing, and concentrate instead on the sensation in your penis. Allow the pleasure to build up but stop immediately you feel you are about to lose control. Relax for a while, still keeping your mind free of fantasies, until the danger of ejaculation has passed, then begin again. Following the same pattern, aim to continue stopping and starting for 15 minutes without orgasm. You may not be able to manage it at first, but keep trying. As you get more practised, you will probably find you have to stop less often. When you have completed three 15-minute sessions on three consecutive occasions (not necessarily one immediately after the other!), proceed to step two.

● Step two involves masturbating with a lubricating jelly, which will heighten sensation, and make ejaculation more difficult to delay. Follow the stop-start technique described in step one until you have completed three 15-minute sessions on three consecutive occasions.

● Step three. You will now have gained a good measure of control. The next step involves masturbating with a dry hand without stopping for 15 minutes before ejaculation. Keep focusing on your penis rather than fantasizing. When you feel yourself getting dangerously excited, don't stop, but instead, change rhythm or alter your strokes in such a way that the pressure to ejaculate fades. Experiment to see which strokes excite you most, and which allow you most control (see Masturbation, p. 86). Work on this step until you have completed three consecutive sessions as before.

● Step four. Now involve your partner. Explain to her what you have been doing and she should find the challenge enjoyable. Lie on your back and get her to masturbate you with a dry hand, as in step one. Concentrate on the sensations in your penis and ask her to stop every time you get too aroused before the 15 minutes is up. Aim is to last for three consecutive 15-minute sessions.

● Step five. Repeat step four, but ask your partner to use a lubricant while she masturbates you. You will find ejaculation much more difficult to control, and you may have to ask her to stop more often. Once you have mastered three consecutive 15-minute sessions, you are ready to try the stop-start technique with intercourse.

● Step six. The best position for delaying ejaculation is with the woman on top. Once you are inside her, ask her to move gently. Put your hands on her hips so that you can let her know with your hands when you want her to stop, and when you are ready for her to start again. Again, aim to last for 15 minutes, but if you can't, don't worry: you can start again once you recover your erection, and the second time around you will probably have more control. During intercourse, concentrate entirely on yourself. Give your partner your full concentration and bring her to orgasm either before or afterwards, with oral or manual stimulation.

● Step seven. Move on to other positions (see p. 98). It is more difficult to delay ejaculation with the man on top, so save this until last.

153

The Squeeze Technique for Delaying Ejaculation

This technique was developed by Masters and Johnson to help men who ejaculate prematurely, and it often succeeds where the stop-start technique fails. In fact, Masters and Johnson found that it cured 98 per cent of the premature ejaculators for whom they prescribed it, within a period of about three months.

The 'squeeze' action is designed to cause your erection to subside, and it is applied every time you get too close to ejaculation. Your partner performs the squeeze by gripping your penis firmly, and pressing with her thumb on the frenulum. This is the place on the underside of the penis where the head joins the shaft. At the same time, she presses on the opposite side of the penis with her forefinger, and with her other fingers curled round the shaft. It is important that she presses fairly hard on the penis and doesn't move her hand while doing so. Too light a touch and any movement could cause you to ejaculate straight away.

● Step one. Get your partner to masturbate you with a dry hand. Any time you get too close to ejaculation, signal to her to stop and squeeze your penis. As with the stop-start technique, aim to last for three consecutive 15-minute sessions before moving on to step two.

● Step two. Get your partner to masturbate you, but this time ask her to use a lubricant. Follow the procedure for step one.

● Step three. Now you are ready for intercourse, but not for thrusting. Instead, lie on your back and ask your partner to sit on top of you, with your penis inside her. Neither of you should move. As soon as you feel the urge to come, your partner should rise off you (this movement is dangerous as it applies stimulation), and immediately hold your penis in the squeeze grip. Repeat the exercise a couple of times before you allow yourself to ejaculate.

● Step four. When you feel more confident about your self-control, ask your partner to move gently while she sits on top of you in the same position. When you feel the urge to ejaculate, she should move off you and squeeze as before, until you can last for 15 minutes without ejaculating.

● Step five. You are now ready to try other positions, but remember that with the man on top, you will have least control. As with the stop-start technique, during intercourse you should focus all attention on yourself. Your partner will not feel neglected if you bring her to orgasm orally or manually either before or after intercourse.

Why do some men ejaculate too soon?

Premature ejaculation is usually caused by anxiety. In an extramarital relationship a man may ejaculate as soon as he penetrates his partner's vagina, despite the fact that he does not have this problem with his wife. This is a sign that he feels guilty about sex with his mistress: the more quickly it is over, the less guilt he imagines he will have to bear. He may also feel frightened that his technique is not good enough, and ejaculating quickly will prevent him from having to reveal his lack of experience.

It may be, too, that the premature ejaculator comes from a family in which sex was thought of as dirty and wrong. As a boy, he may have been punished for masturbating, and may have taught himself to come quickly to lessen the chance of being found out and to minimize the guilt he felt at his own pleasure. Someone who has conditioned himself to behave like this will find it very difficult to change.

Another possible cause of premature ejaculation is the fear of getting too close to another person. Intimacy always brings with it the risk of loss, and the unbearable pain attendant on that loss. Subconsciously, a man who gets sex over with quickly may be trying to protect himself from close involvement. Of course, there are also women with the same fear, and very often these women satisfy a hidden need in themselves by teaming up with premature ejaculators.

When is 'premature ejaculation' not a problem?

When it doesn't feel like premature ejaculation to either of you. There is no rule about how long you should last once you are inside a woman's vagina, and you may be worrying needlessly. There are several ways of improving lovemaking without resorting to any special techniques. Firstly, make sure you spend plenty of time kissing, caressing and arousing your partner before you enter her. If she does not normally come with you inside her – and the majority of women do not – then give her enough time to do so before penetration. Stimulate her clitoris with your fingers, then tongue, or do whatever she likes.

Once you are inside her, she will be really ready for you to come anyway, so it will be no disappointment to her if you don't last half an hour (see the section on Vaginal ache, p. 44). Both of you can now concentrate on your own pleasure. After your orgasm, relax

together for as long as it takes for you to get another erection, and then you can begin to make love again. This time you will probably find that you have more control over ejaculation and can last much longer. This works particularly well with younger men who are more excitable and less experienced. As you grow older, you will be able to last longer.

Another way of prolonging intercourse is to avoid deep thrusting movements, and to move very gently. Practise resting with your erect penis inside your partner's vagina, occasionally moving your hips. Some women who do not usually come with a penis inside them will orgasm like this, because they find the suspense unbearably exciting.

Can over-control be a problem?

Premature ejaculation is a widespread problem. The reverse, delayed ejaculation, affects a comparatively small number of men. It is not often regarded as a problem because, after all, there are enormous benefits to both partners if a man can last a long time before he ejaculates. As you grow older, you will find that you are naturally able to last longer. You may find that the ability to come quickly deserts you altogether, and that you need prolonged and more vigorous stimulation before you climax. None of this should worry you.

However, if you repeatedly have sex without ejaculating and it is beginning to upset you, you may need to retrain yourself to ejaculate in the presence

of, and then inside, your partner. A therapist might recommend that you begin by masturbating to orgasm back to back, then do the same holding your partner close to you. Repeat the exercise, each time coming closer to her vagina. Then let your partner stimulate you until you are close to ejaculating, and quickly penetrate her so that you orgasm inside. You should always wait until you are fully aroused before entering your partner, and remember that with the man on top you will be able to exercise less control over yourself.

If this method does not work, you should seek the help of a therapist, who will explore with you the underlying causes of 'ejaculatory incompetence', as it is known, and prescribe a special programme for you and your partner to follow.

Why do men sometimes lose interest in sex?

Because male sexual response is more straightforward than female sexual response, it is somehow assumed that men are always ready to have sex 'on demand'. Their partners can be very disappointed to find that this is not necessarily so. This can be a problem, particularly for women in their middle years who have developed strong sexual drive. A partner who repeatedly is too tired or uninspired for sex can cause such women deep unhappiness and frustration.

The problem can be partly due to conditioning. In the case of a second marriage, for instance, where a couple have been passionate adulterous lovers and are now married themselves, the man may revert to the staid old ways he knew with his first wife, with whom he rarely made love. It could be that he is capable of passion only with someone who is not his wife, and who carries with her the excitement of the forbidden. Unless the new wife can help him overcome the problem, and perhaps persuade him to seek professional help, their relationship, like his previous marriage, will be doomed.

Although every man is likely to suffer a temporary loss of interest in sex from time to time, due to the stress of overwork, or to feeling tired or under the weather, the cause of a more sustained loss of interest probably lies in the relationship itself. No one can make love with someone they feel angry with or hostile towards, and sex out of a sense of matrimonial duty with someone who bores you is not as much fun as masturbation.

At what age is a man at the peak of sexual potency?

It depends what you mean by the phrase 'sexual potency'. At the age of 18 a man may have spontaneous and very firm erections that are hardly lost at ejaculation so that he is ready for penetration again almost straight away. But no man of this age can have the experience that makes a sensitive and skilful lover, and younger men usually have less staying power.

As a man ages, he needs more time and stimulation to achieve an erection and to orgasm, and develops more staying power. This means that lovemaking will naturally last longer, which gives scope for more variety. Lovemaking can become gentle, sensitive, adventurous and prolonged: more satisfying to both parties.

From the age of about 50, it may take a man 24 hours after he has ejaculated before he can get another erection, and after the age of 60, the erection will become noticeably less firm. None of this diminishes the sexual potential of a man who has developed a good technique and cares for the person he is with, and a man can carry on satisfying himself and his partner, and learning more about how to do so, well into old age.

What should a man do if he fears he is a clumsy lover?

Read the sections on Female orgasm (see p. 38) and Understanding a woman's feelings (see p. 52). Clumsiness is often due to inexperience and lack of confidence. Be gentle with your partner, and take time to explore her body. Never rush lovemaking: she will only be able to open up to you if she trusts you not to hurt her. Wait until she is fully aroused, or until you have brought her to orgasm, before penetration. If you don't know how to do this, ask her how she responds to your caresses. Be tentative in your experiments until you both find out what pleases her best. When you discover how to please her, your own pleasure and confidence will increase, you will feel more relaxed, and your clumsiness will disappear.

Are there such things as aphrodisiacs?

The short answer is no. Powdered rhino horn, wolf's penis, the velvet that grows on a stag's antlers, are just three of some 900 substances reputed at one time or another to have the power of sexual arousal. However, it has been said that the body's most powerful sexual organ is the mind, and if you sit down with your lover to slurp oysters from their shells, or to suck mayonnaise off asparagus spears, the resemblance of the food to human genitals, and of eating it to oral sex, might suggest what you could do next. Perhaps open a bottle of champagne?

Index

ACKNOWLEDGEMENTS

*All the photographs in this book were
specially taken by Steve Hathaway for Reed Consumer
Books Limited with the exception of those
appearing on the following pages:*

*Camera Press 10-11, 17; Image Bank/Jan Cobb 132;
Tony Stone Worldwide 61, 142.*

Editor SIAN FACER

Art Editor SANDRA HORTH

Designer PETER BUTLER

Production CHERYL COOPER

Picture research JENNY FAITHFULL,
JULIA PASHLEY

Special photography STEVE HATHAWAY

Stylist, hair and make-up PATTI HARRISON

Illustrations PATRICIA LUDLOW